AIR SUPPORT SAFETY:

AN AIRBORNE PUBLIC SAFETY PILOT'S QUEST TO REDUCE FLIGHT RISKS & INCREASE MISSION SUCCESS

BRYAN SMITH

AIR SUPPORT
SAFETY:
AN AIRBORNE PUBLIC SAFETY PILOT'S QUEST TO REDUCE FLIGHT RISKS & INCREASE MISSION SUCCESS

BRYAN SMITH

ISBN: 978-1-7367065-0-3

Published by Wright Publishing Group, Inc.
1120 Pinellas Bayway South #205
St. Petersburg, FL 33715
Send inquiries to Lisa A. Wrigh
Email: airbeat@publicsafetyaviation.org

Printed and bound in the United States of America.

Editorial Director & Editor: Lisa A. Wright
Art Director & Graphic Designer: Zack R. Mullikin

Part of proceeds to benefit the Airborne Public Safety Association.

Visit www.PublicSafetyAviation.org and www.AirSupportSafety.com for more information.

DEDICATION/ACKNOWLEDGEMENTS

When I started working on aviation safety for the Airborne Public Safety Association (APSA), it was more than a bit overwhelming. There were so many questions that needed to be answered and problems that needed to be solved; the only thing I knew for sure was that I did not have all the answers. This book contains the results of my quest to find those answers and it has been a journey that involved more people than can be counted. Members from around the world have continuously worked with me in every aspect of APSA's Safety Program. Aviation professionals from within the Federal Aviation Administration's FAASTeam, the International Helicopter Safety Foundation (IHSF), the Helicopter Association International (HAI) and many others have generously offered me valuable information and assistance. The APSA Board of Directors and staff have consistently given me the support and resources needed to make its safety program effective. To all of you who have contributed to the information in this book, thank you.

APSA CEO/Executive Director Dan Schwarzbach and publishing partner Lisa Wright have edited everything I have written for APSA, including all of the articles in this book. They have turned my chunks of coal into diamonds for a decade. Without all of their dedicated work and talent, these articles would never have conveyed their intended message so successfully. Thank you.

Most importantly, my family has supported the long hours spent working on APSA projects without so much as a word of discontent. My children, already suffering the pain of being a police officer's kids, endure the late nights their dad is laboring over the computer or travelling for yet another seminar. If it were not for my wife, I would not be a pilot, let alone safety program manager or author. She has not only supported my decisions but also pushed me towards my goals when I needed it. Stacy, Maya and Zack: I love you more than anything...even flying. Thank you for making this happen.

CONTENTS

PREFACE

This book contains safety articles written by Sgt. Bryan Smith for the Airborne Public Safety Association's bi-monthly journal called *Air Beat* Magazine. Bryan is not only a full-time chief pilot of a law enforcement air support unit, he is also APSA's Safety Program Manager and instructor. APSA was founded in 1968 as an educational organization whose mission is "to serve, save and protect from the air" and one way to accomplish that is through its safety education and outreach.

Bryan has spent his career developing and implementing safety solutions for operators and pilots. His passion for aviation safety and training has given him the opportunity to meet and instruct safety classes to hundreds of airborne law enforcement aviators in the United States, Canada, Europe (Belgium, Netherlands, Germany and Latvia), Africa and Brazil. In 2017, Bryan earned the Helicopter Association International's prestigious Safety Award for his efforts.

The profession of public safety aviation has wide-ranging responsibilities; the most important is to perform the mission successfully and arrive home safe. Bryan shares a story of how he handled an inflight emergency that turned out well because of training that started with a 1,800-word magazine article he read in *Air Beat* from someone else. Bryan's collection of safety articles reminds aviators that they can also counter flight risks with learning, listening and training—training from the classroom, books, magazines, conversations, online resources and real-world experience. He says the best pilots have the motivation to seek out training and go beyond the minimum requirements. The best pilots are ones who don't think he or she is the best because there is still so much to learn. The best pilots, mechanics, TFOs and aircrew members are all of you who are reading this, because you want to get better.

CHAPTER 1

SAFETY CULTURE

Over the last decades, we have seen many changes in the public safety aviation industry. New equipment and new tactics have managed to flourish despite an economy that has done little to help our industry. The world continues to change around us and, like good warriors, we adjust with those challenges to stay in the fight.

New concepts have taken the main stage in aviation safety. Safety management systems (SMS) were a new idea in 2005, and the first toolkit from the Airborne Public Safety Association and the International Helicopter Safety Team wasn't published until 2009. Today, few in our business have not heard of SMS or the associated concepts of just culture, hazard analysis, flight risk assessment tools, etc.

Still, tired old mantras like "there are no new ways to crash aircraft" remain painfully valid. Despite lowered accident and fatality rates over the last few years, we still find ourselves at too many funerals wondering if something could have been done to prevent another tragedy.

A critical part of any SMS is a functional connection between safety manager and the training manager. APSA's Training Program Manager Don Roby and I have tried to practice what we preach by keeping the APSA training and safety initiatives a seamless effort. Keeping with the SMS principle of risk assessment, we have focused on the highest risk categories over the years including, inadvertent flight into instrument metrological conditions (IIMC), training accidents and wire strike accidents. The numbers in those three categories have decreased but still remain the top threats to our safety.

The one thing that has remained a constant in our industry is the importance of people. The information we publish is a waste of paper if people do not use it. Even in the age of unmanned aircraft, the key component to everything we do is the individual who connects the material provided with their actions to perform the job better, with a safer outcome. Human factors is the one common thread that ties academic safety concepts to the real world. Textbook information has no effect on safety if it cannot be applied to our daily tasks in a realistic manner.

We have talked for decades about the risk of flying or doing maintenance while fatigued. When I ask audiences how many have a fatigue policy that covers maximum duty day and minimum rest time, most people raise their hands. When I ask the same group how many have recently violated that fatigue policy at least once, most people raise their hands. Why? We must ask ourselves, "What would happen if I told my boss I was too tired to fly?"

Another old enemy is IIMC. As an industry, we have been talking about it, and will, for years. We have increased our understanding of why it happens and how dangerous it is. Yet incidents continue.

A lingering problem with IIMC (and many other emergencies) is connecting knowledge with personal performance in an actual incident. The key is training, but not just any kind of training: realistic scenario-based training. Our performance is influenced by stress, and with that knowledge, we can design training to help us perform better in emergencies like IIMC.

SAFETY CULTURE

Many of the errors that lead to IIMC accidents start on the ground. When crews are evaluating flight risks, basic human factors come into play and limit our ability to make accurate and objective risk assessments. These errors can lead us to launch when we shouldn't or cancel flights unnecessarily. This is especially true when preparing to launch on critical incidents.

As long as we've been talking about SMS, we've been preaching about the importance of a safety culture. Everyone knows that a safety culture is important, yet so many of us still work in environments that need improvement. Why is there a disconnect? Often, we simply do not know our culture needs improvement or how to make it better.

To do our job well with a safe outcome, we simply cannot forget that we are all human. Recognizing human needs and limitations is not acceptance of weakness; it is smart risk management. In many ways, human factors are an attribute, not a hindrance. Human factors are not dangerous, but failing to understand or ignoring their limitations is. Aircrew training and crew resource management are effective ways to keep us within those limitations during operations in the air and on the ground.

Another limitation we would be smart to remember is our resilience to mental stress. For several months after I was involved in an accident in 2009, I was haunted by visions of my children crying at my funeral every time I strapped into an aircraft. The next year, I responded to a fatal airplane crash scene involving friends. I was again haunted by visions of the scene for several months. In both cases, I felt I was strong enough to "tough it out" and work through the issue. But not only was it unhealthy for me to continue without talking to someone, it was unsafe.

It is an undeniable but often forgettable fact that we must remember our personal human needs if we wish to be fit enough to protect the rest of the world. In 10 years, I hope we will look back at this time as a turning point. We have the tools, ideas and means to make significant changes in aviation safety for our industry. There is willingness, even desire, to strive to make aviation safer. The key is to consider the person—the human factors—that govern how information and knowledge can actually be used in the real world in which we work. Perhaps that will be the key that opens the door to a whole new era of unprecedented safety.

COOKIE'S SAFETY CULTURE:
Using Standards to Reduce Cloud of Danger

Our aviation unit said goodbye to a pilot who had decided to retire. To us, he was "Cookie," a gruff man with a sweet tooth. For 40 years, he had cheated death serving his country, from flying Hueys in the jungles of Vietnam to a long and distinguished career as a law enforcement officer, commander and pilot. As I reflected on the decades of risk-saturated work Cookie survived, I wondered how I might be able to do the same.

Cookie, like most pilots, had a few interesting quirks. To say he liked things to be in order would be an understatement. For example, the light switch for the hangar lights in our office was one of many throughout the building, so it would sometimes be in the down position even though the lights were on. Cookie would correct it 100% of the time.

When I asked Cookie how he managed to stay safe for so long, he credited his original military training, which stressed completing every task to a standard every time. I realized that the very habit we'd made fun of was what had kept him safe for decades. Cookie stayed safe by doing everything right, putting everything in the correct place, turning every switch the right way, completing every task according to the standard, every single time. Many people (myself included) do not have the mental athleticism to hold such a high standard perfectly for decades. So I started to think about how others could apply Cookie's advice to their careers.

> "Inherent danger does not influence our safety behavior unless we recognize that danger, decide it is unacceptable and label it a risk."

A safety culture is one of the critical components of a successful safety system. Culture determines what we label as a risk. It also dictates what safety behavior should be conducted during our daily business. A poor safety culture either fails to define risks properly or falls short of actually creating effective and consistently safe behavior. Decades ago, driving in a vehicle without a seatbelt was not defined as a risk by most of society, and many people did not wear one. Over time, society defined the failure to wear a seatbelt as a risk, and appropriate behavior followed that definition. The danger involved in failure to wear a seatbelt did not change. Inherent danger does not influence our safety behavior unless we recognize that danger, decide it is unacceptable and label it a risk.

Many law enforcement aviation risks are not as clearly or appropriately defined as the above example. Often, the risk is identified and designated as such only after metal is bent or lives are lost. This is in part due to the notion that what we do is hazardous, and there is nothing we can do about it. Safety programs based on the limited scope of a single event are restricted to dealing with only the final link of a long chain of problems. Fortunately, this is changing because our definition of risk is evolving.

Following the crash of the Space Shuttle Columbia in 2003, an extensive investigation was launched to uncover the cause of the accident. The cause was traced back through mechanical component failures (as would be expected) but continued into the deep tissue of NASA's safety culture. The review board showed how the view of safety had changed. The danger of space flight was no longer considered something to be accepted as normal, but a risk that must be addressed.

"They were convinced, without study, that nothing could be done about such an emergency," the report stated. "The intellectual curiosity and skepticism that a solid safety culture requires was almost entirely absent." The report went on to say that such a culture was "incompatible with an organization that deals with high-risk technology."

A similar response was made by the National Transportation Safety Board in a high-profile law enforcement crash years ago. The governing agency was faulted for failing to have a functioning safety program. The report determined that part of the probable cause was the agency's "deficiencies in... safety-related policies, including lack of a requirement for a risk assessment at any point during the mission." The report recommended state aviation officials "develop and implement risk assessment and management procedures specific to their operations."

This was not the first Space Shuttle lost and far from the first helicopter lost to similar circumstances. These findings have illustrated that we no longer view our profession as dangerous, but one challenged by risk. Writing off an accident as an unavoidable cost of doing a hazardous business is no longer a defense. Fortunately, by identifying and defining the risks, we have taken the first step in addressing them.

Our tradition of reactionary safety culture has provided us with countless do's and do not's. The sheer volume of all safety related information in public safety aviation is so vast it would be naïve to think it all could be constantly kept in the forefront of our minds to be accessed whenever we need it.

But what if those thousands of components could be used to build a machine capable of addressing risk in every aspect of our profession?

We have just that machine: the safety management system. SMS can take all of the little bits and pieces and put them together to address an entire operation in a clear and consistent manner. Such a program can counter the cloud of danger that surrounds our public safety aviation profession. It is the answer to our collective refusal to expect unavoidable losses.

MY BROTHER'S KEEPER

The only way we will all survive our careers in public safety aviation is by taking care of one another. That means not just engaging in the easy, positive stuff, but also having the tough conversations and making the difficult calls. We all need to be ready to go out of our comfort zone to protect our brothers and sisters. Probably the most difficult part for all of us is to listen when someone has that conversation with us. It is unlikely we'll know how much we need to hear what is being said.

Self-monitoring of our limitations is so infested with failure points that we need to expect this protective barrier to collapse and prepare for it.

A few years ago, I went through some major life changes—new job, moving the family to a new city, a schedule that already did not allow spare time. To stay caught up, I stayed up later and set my alarm to wake up earlier. To minimize the time spent eating, I found myself hitting the fast-food drive-through more often while racing between meetings.

The time normally allotted to exercise was more and more often diverted to computer work.

Despite all these efforts to spend more time working, I soon started missing meetings and deadlines. I missed paying some bills and forgot to do minor maintenance on equipment around the house, which caused it to fail completely. I actually booked a flight to the wrong city for an APSA event. It wasn't until I made those fatal, big errors that I realized I needed to make a change. I was lucky the errors did not occur in an aircraft.

In 2017, APSA spent the entire year talking about human factors in their publications and educational classes. I know less sleep and exercise and poor diet decrease work efficiency. Yet I pushed forward, fooling myself that I had everything under control. How did I let it happen?

The first place I turn when I have questions about human factors is APSA Aeromedical Liaison Dudley Crosson. He reminded me of some important information. One research project found reducing sleep periods to four to six hours per night for two weeks was enough to create consistent degradation in performance levels, matching someone who had not slept at all in two days. Another study showed that even with eight hours of sleep, our performance starts to decrease after 10 hours of being awake. The study further indicated 17 hours after waking up, our performance is equivalent to that of someone with a blood alcohol concentration of 0.05 percent. The performance of a person going a full 24 hours without sleep is equal to a BAC of 0.10 percent. Analysis of nurse performance showed accident rate increases significantly after nine hours of work and doubles at the 12-hour mark.

What about the time I saved hitting the drive-through for lunch? I might have saved a few minutes shoveling down a hamburger between meetings, but processed food strains the system and slows you down for the rest of the day. The British Psychological Society published a report in 2014 that showed a marked difference in creative problem-solving performance between adults who ate a diet high in fruits and vegetables and those who did not. Unfortunately, I don't think the lettuce on my cheeseburger counts.

And that time I skipped exercise so I could click away at the laptop some more? I probably don't need to explain how a decrease in exercise leads to a further decline in energy, concentration and general mental capacity. For me, the combination of reduced sleep, poor diet choices and missed exercise created a trifecta of misery that ensured I would not finish the work for which I was sacrificing my health.

The fact that fatigue, poor diet and lack of exercise decrease performance capabilities is not new information. We all know these things are bad for us. The problem is, we often have limited awareness of how these conditions impact us when they come up.

Research has shown we do not recognize our own performance limitations until it is too late. Often, we will not know we are too tired, stressed or overtasked until we make some sort of physical tasking error. We may drop something, cross the centerline while driving or forget an important step in a process before we start to think our performance may have reached its limit. Even then, we are rarely short of excuses to explain the mistake and reinforce the inaccurate conclusion that we are still competent.

What's more, the effects of pressure on our performance rarely act uniformly. Stressors such as fatigue and overtasking hit us at unpredictable intervals, like an engine in need of maintenance that starts to miss or skip periodically. Between the skips, we tell ourselves the event was an odd, one-time event and move on because the inconsistency has stopped. Human error is just like that failing engine—we do not know when the next "miss" will occur. When it happens again, it may be a more significant failure or the timing could be at a moment when we cannot afford a performance degradation.

When it comes to fatigue, physical skills are not the first thing to go. Decision-making is corrupted long before. In research by sleep expert Dr. Gregory Belenky, soldiers were able to aim accurately and hit a target after 48 hours of fragmented sleep. However, their situational awareness was degraded. The fatigued soldiers couldn't make good decisions about what target to hit or why. The loss in situational awareness started to occur around the study's 24-hour mark. At 48 hours, operational performance was decreased 50 percent on average.

Belenky's research illustrates a major factor in friendly fire incidents and operational errors, such as the Jessica Lynch convoy incident in 2003. The convoy drivers were able to operate their vehicles properly despite fatigue, but a loss of situational awareness and decision-making abilities caused wrong turns that led to their capture.

In many of the loss of control accidents in our industry, the error is usually not a lack of piloting skill, but improper decision-making and situational awareness. Still, we concentrate on physical skills for both monitoring human performance limits and determining errors.

The factors reducing our human performance also make it difficult to detect we are approaching our limit. Cognizance of our condition and performance requires mental attention and analysis. If the limiting factor is overtasking, we already have a deficit of mental resources for self-monitoring. The diversion is especially powerful if the external tasks are the stressful, life-and-death varieties common in public safety aviation that tend to dominate our attention.

The perception of our current condition can be deceiving under intense task loads. According to Dr. Jim Horne, a large number of fighter pilots who performed well during dogfights crashed during the Battle for Britain while returning to base or during landing even though the tasks were considerably less complex. The pilots, who were often sleep deprived, would stay alert when engaged in intense aerial combat. But once the mental stimulation waned, mental performance trailed off to the point where simple tasks led to accidents.

In one survey of critical care nurses working 12-hour shifts, 96 percent reported having a motor vehicle accident, or nearly having one, while driving home from work the previous year. I am reminded of how many officers we lose while they are heading home at the end of their shift. In a 2011 study by the International Helicopter Safety Team, "repositioning/return to base" was the second leading activity being conducted when crashes occurred.

In Belenky's fatigue research, he also interviewed the soldiers under observation. Even when showing severe signs of fatigue-related perform-ance degradation, most soldiers reported they did not feel fatigued. This highlights how the problem can bite even the most professional among us: being educated on our limitations and being aware of our condition are two different things.

The closer we get to a limit, the less likely we are to know it. I have said too many times, "I'll take a break when I need it" or "I don't feel great, but I'm okay now and I'll tell you if I get too tired (sick, upset, hun-gry) to fly." This is the kind of macho self-delusion that leads many of us to an early grave. It must end. The gauge we use to monitor our human en-gine is fatally flawed. The only way to monitor these factors and prevent exceeding our limits is through measuring devices not influenced by our condition. Unit policy and CRM are two such solutions.

I'm not big on writing huge policy manuals. But well written, safety management system-driven policy provides operational limitations that prevent us from exceeding human factors-related capabilities.

If we only set limits in our head or through unwritten doctrine of "how we do business," the limits will be adjusted to meet operational needs, not human needs. This is especially true in major events like hurricanes or lengthy manhunts when we excuse ourselves from common sense because we believe it's okay to do whatever it takes to get the job done. Policy does not allow for excuses. It is there in black and white no matter how much fatigue, stress, overtasking or a poor lunch choice is affecting us.

The policies, however, only work if they are well written and we are smart enough to apply them to ourselves every time, not just when it is convenient.

The most powerful defense against the trap of our own human lim-its is our coworkers. Twelve years ago, I went to work when I was not feeling well. I thought I could tough it out. After a short time, my TFO examined me from across the desk for a few minutes before asking how I felt. I told him I was fine. He said, "Bubba, I ain't flying with you tonight. Go home." I sat back and looked at him, defeated. Then I did the first smart thing I'd done all night. I went home.

Recently, I was walking out the door after a series of long workdays. The next day was my day off, but I asked the crew working the next day to call me in the morning if I could help with a minor technical issue we'd been working on. The newest member of our unit said, "Absolutely not. Get some sleep and play with your kids." I paused, chuckled and said "okay." He was just as correct as my TFO had been more than a decade ago.

How would you react if a coworker told you that you looked too tired, angry, sick, stressed or distracted to fly or do maintenance on an aircraft? If you saw a coworker that needed a break, would you say something? Have any of you in a supervisor's role ever turned a blind eye to such a situation because you didn't have a good option to fill the person's position for the day? Ever let someone work even though they were obviously tired, ill or stressed because you wanted to believe them when they said they were okay? When filling out a flight risk assessment form, have you ever indicated another person had enough rest and no medication needs, stress nor illness without asking him or her, just to speed up the process? How did you know the coworker was okay?

These simple but sometimes uncomfortable situations offer us a chance to either care for one another or stand by and watch our brother or sister walk blindly towards disaster. I have excused myself with standbys like, "that's their choice" or "it's none of my business." But if we don't take care of one another, who will? And frankly, if I'm flying with you in the same aircraft or you are doing maintenance on something I'm going to fly, it is absolutely my business.

Human performance limitations are like bullets. We can sit in class and look at them all day, learning about all the damage they can do. But in a gunfight, we will never know one is headed our way until it hits us. Establish rules of engagement that minimize our exposure to being hit—good rules, created out of a thoughtful process by people with operational knowledge. Most importantly, protect each other. Pull one another out of the line of fire. When you pull me to safety, I may even resist, because I don't see the bullet coming.

TACTICS AUDIT:
Tradition is a Powerful Influence

Aviation and law enforcement are professions rich in tradition. I consider myself an aviation tradition junkie. I still think Ray Ban sunglasses are the only reasonable choice for a self-respecting pilot, and the only jacket I wear is leather Avirex A-2 with WWII nose art on the back. I have shelves full of aviation history books, including a beloved copy of Wolfgang Langewiesche's *Stick and Rudder* that is dog-eared and tattered from years of use. Next to it is *Low Level Hell* by Hugh Mills, which I still consider required reading for any new law enforcement flight crewmember. I take pride in still being able to work an EA6B flight computer (the manual one, not the electric calculator). If anyone were to ask me, I think the most beautiful object ever made by mankind was the F4U Corsair.

For the most part, these traditions do no harm and actually form the foundation of the skills and knowledge that keep us safe and effective. Sometimes, however, our dedication to the past can keep us from reaching our fullest potential.

Years ago, I was flying with a new TFO who I had been training for several months. He had gone through a training program I'd helped develop years ago while working with a very accomplished TFO at another agency. One of the more challenging tasks I have found to master in the art of TFOing (yes, that is a verb) is setting the gain and level (brightness) on the thermal imager. During this particular call, I glanced over at the monitor and saw a beautiful, crisp picture that was allowing the TFO to pick out a small thermal target in thick trees on a hot, muggy summer evening. I was instantly pleased with myself for having passed on the knowledge needed for this difficult task.

"That's a great picture, man," I said. "What are your levels set at?" When he answered, I was in disbelief, as one of the settings was opposite of what I'd been recommending for months. I even made him show me. Under the dim green glow of my liplight, I experienced a moment of enlightenment. I had been stuck using the techniques needed to set up imagers from an older system. My TFO trainee had the sense to listen to my instruction but examine it with a critical eye.

This was a tactics issue, but the same scenario occurs regarding safety issues. Often, safety and mission efficiency are inseparable.

One of the great traditions of public safety aviation is the art of compromise. We have always found balance between what needs to be done, the limitations of our equipment and the inherent risk involved in engaging in our work from the air. There is also a great amount of respect for those responsible for finding that balance in the early days of public safety aviation, when everything was new and the tactics had to be invented from scratch. These compromise-defined mission profiles have become time-honored traditions.

Some studies have shown that our traditions begin to tie into our value system. Compromising safety for mission requirements in law enforcement is frequently considered a badge of bravery, something not to be questioned. According to fatigue risk management expert Philippa Gander, even if the tradition carries high risk that can be mitigated with new techniques or equipment, it is more psychologically stressful for us to question the traditional activity than to face the actual dangers involved. The risks that were originally addressed tend to become perceived as normal and permanent. It is no longer a risk to be dealt with; it is an unquestionable cost of doing business. When the conditions of the original compromise change, we are reluctant to reevaluate the equation.

When I started working for the Gainesville (FL) Police Department in 2004, we had an Inframetrics Mk.1 thermal imager. In the right hands and with the right tactics, the camera successfully found many a bad guy. But the limitations of the system required a compromise: we could not be higher than 1,000 feet AGL over the jungle-like terrain we patrolled. Often we needed to sneak down even lower when the subject was hiding. In the daytime in Florida, we didn't even bother turning it on. Soon we upgraded to a newer system and finally upgraded even further to a FLIR 8500, which gave us at least twice the range and daytime capability. Still, we were flying using the same tactics and altitudes we needed for the Smithsonian-bound Mk.1, and never thought of using the new system during the daytime. Why?

Over time we had forgotten the tactics we used were the result of compromise based on the limitations of a system we were no longer using. We had not been at 800 feet at night with the old system because of some undeniable law, it was simply because that was the limit of the camera. It was my TFO who said to me one night, "Hey, why don't we climb up to 1,200 feet and try this thing from there?" Not only did it work great from that altitude (and even higher), but also we found several tactical advantages that actually increased our mission success rate. From a higher altitude, the screen was more stable, the rate of rotation of the image on the screen was slower, and we had more angles to work with when looking through trees or between buildings. It was also undeniably safer working with a little more air between the ground and us.

It wasn't until I later visited the very successful Brevard County (FL) Sheriff's Office Aviation Unit, which has been awarded the FLIR Vision Award of the Year award several times, that my eyes were opened to the idea of using the new thermal imager during the day. I asked the unit's members how they managed to get such great camera operators. One of the first things I was told was that they use the FLIR at all times. In retrospect, it seems so simple, but at the time it was a foreign idea to me. The tactical compromises I made when I started working had simply not allowed higher altitudes or daytime camera operations. I needed to do a tactics audit.

Every once in a while, we need to step back and look at how we conduct business from an objective viewpoint. We must lay everything on the table and ask why each parameter of tactics, training or policy is done the way it is and if new knowledge, techniques or equipment can be utilized to improve the items. Most of the time, we will find the traditional way of doing things is still the best. Once in a while, however, we will find that something has changed and an opportunity exists to be safer and more effective. Thermal imager settings and tactics, as mentioned, are frequently one of the items that will drive these changes simply because their effectiveness increases exponentially with each new generation of equipment.

Night vision goggles are another example of a game-changer. When the crew I was working with first received NVGs, the question was: if they allowed us to see better at night, could we lower our altitude to daytime patrol levels? We went out on several training flights and tried it. We tried three configurations: 500 feet with the thermal imager and NVGs, 500 feet with the searchlight and NVGs, and 1,000 feet with the thermal imager and NVGs. Our TFOs found they could most effectively work a call from 1,000 feet with the camera. Again, it was a surprise to us. Lower had always meant better. Unfortunately, lower is also traditionally attributed to a perception of greater flying skills and dedication to the mission. These are strong illusions entrenched in tradition, not the reality of the choices we have in today's public safety aviation world.

As we add new and more capable pieces of equipment to our toolbox, new points of failure are added to the long list of "what ifs" we must train for. For example, while NVGs increase safety significantly and augment tactical capabilities, they also add a number of new possible equipment malfunctions and opportunities for human error that did not exist before. Those points of failure need to be recognized and mitigated through training, tactics and policy. The same can be said for new radio systems, avionics, mapping systems and anything else being added to the tactical scenario. Even if an equipment malfunction does not directly affect the safe operation of an aircraft, it presents a distraction that could lead to bigger problems. These issues change the tactical compromise governing how we do our work and should be considered in an audit of mission techniques.

I still find areas where my own perceptions unknowingly influence what I do in the cockpit. Chief Pilot Richard Bray of the Alachua County (FL) Sheriff's Office once gave a presentation about an emergency landing he had to make in an OH-58. One of the most striking points he made was that he had been flying at 800 feet AGL during daytime patrol. It was something he mentioned almost in passing. I have always flown rotorcraft at 500 feet during the day. Why? That's the way we'd always done it, and when you're looking for a person hiding during the day using the Mk.1 eyeball, 500 feet is about right.

But recently, while searching for a minivan carrying a homicide suspect, I asked myself why I was at 500 feet. We routinely flew similar calls successfully in our Cessna 210 from 1,000 feet. I increased altitude a bit, and not only could we see vehicles just fine from a higher altitude, we could see more of them at once. A week later I found myself searching for a vehicle at 500 feet again, and the only reason I'd reverted back to my traditional flight profile was that I was keeping an eye on a nearby 800-foot tower.

Tradition is a powerful influence in our behavior. Usually, it helps us work under the guidance of the collective knowledge and experiences of the entire industry. Sometimes, it keeps us from improving our profession.

PERFORMING A TACTICS AUDIT

The following items are recommended when performing a tactics audit:

- When you take the time to sit around the table and do an audit of your tactics, training and policies, look specifically at the strategies developed as a compromise between capabilities and mission requirements. Ask yourself if the factors governing either side of the equation have changed. Hint: If you have added any new equipment within the last few years, those parameters have changed.

- If you decide to try a new or modified tactic or training method, practice it in training at least three or four times before doing it on an actual mission. Even small changes in how you work can create significant distractions in the cockpit or hangar floor.

- For training techniques, have at least two or three CFIs or aircrew trainers (i.e. chief TFOs) spend time analyzing every aspect of the new technique or policy. Think of anything that could go wrong, how to identify those issues as early as possible, and what intervention the instructor can make to correct it.

- When training new aircrew members, make sure you can explain why you perform each technique and tactic in addition to how to perform it. Make sure new unit members are comfortable asking questions about how business is conducted. Be open to the concept that new perspectives and "fresh eyes" are valuable resources in keeping your agency's capabilities and safety on the leading edge.

- Visit neighboring units, host training days and attend APSA functions. When you do, ask others how they do business. Ask vendors how their customers are using new equipment. The information obtained from others in airborne law enforcement can often lead to significant, positive changes.

THE HUMAN ELEMENT:
Aeromedical Science Is Integral Part of Safety

Safety management systems are not books on a shelf; they are a way of doing business. Often repeated variations of that statement have turned it into a mantra of safety managers throughout the industry. It seems like an easy concept, but putting it into practice can be challenging. How can we take what we know and use it to influence what we do? Each of us does business differently. However, there is one universal constant in all of our operations, whether they are complex SAR missions, surveillance, patrol support or even UAS missions: the human element.

In addressing risk management in our own operations, I'd like to take a minute to see how we can take some of this information and insert it into the context of an SMS.

In the book *Worth a Second Look*, Lieutenant Colonel Andy Woodrow discusses the limitations of our eyes in relation to critical collision avoidance tasks. Many of us fly in congested airspace. In addition to normal airspace congestion, what we do often draws the attention of media aircraft, EMS helicopters, fire, additional law enforcement aircraft, UAS and even curious civilians. Worse yet, we are all operating without any air traffic control separation assistance more often than not. Unfortunately, we have lost peers in this very scenario in tragic midair collisions.

Many of us have fought for funding to purchase traffic collision avoidance systems. When asked why we need so much money for equipment and installation, we are only armed with an accident report or two and a stern warning that it is "a safety issue." A lack of concrete evidence, typically due to the fact that such an accident has never occurred at our agency, usually dooms the argument to the "future plans" list, which is where ideas go to die.

In a safety management system, we run hazard information through the "probability (likelihood)-severity (consequences)" matrix to assess risk. This helps us prioritize what hazards we need to address and makes the argument for addressing high-priority items more concrete and less subjective. Woodrow's book gives us the exact information

> "There is one universal constant in all of our operations, whether they are complex SAR missions, surveillance, patrol support or even UAS missions: the human element."

we need to establish the probability side of that equation in a scientific and objective manner.

When developing an intervention or mitigation for a risk, we need to specifically target lowering probability and/or severity. There's not much we can do to lessen the severity of a midair collision. However, we can lessen the probability of the events. TCAS is one option. TFO and CRM training is another.

First, an untrained TFO can divert a pilot's attention from scanning for other traffic as he or she tries to help manage the mission on the ground. Second, a trained TFO can assist the pilot in scanning for aircraft. I can't count the number of times other aircraft were picked up by my "TFOCAS" before I saw them.

Make these items specific interventions applied through training and policy. Those training and policy items should be hashed out through the safety committee. In this manner, an SMS allows us to make collision avoidance a matter of normal operations and crew training. As a side note, the information on visual scanning techniques and limitations has some useful tactical applications that apply just as well when looking for targets on the ground.

As you develop your safety training, policies, procedures and equipment upgrades (mitigations), take time to consider what other components of the operation might affect the strategy. Can your crews actually carry out the procedure under the stress of the emergency being addressed? Will another aircraft component failure, such as electrical power, render this mitigation ineffective when it is needed? This makes the suggested mitigation far more realistic and easier to integrate into the existing operational system.

Dudley Crosson is the guy I turn to when I need real information on aeromedical issues. The reason I use the term "real" is that he can always provide me with facts. In the safety world, we too often rely on our own evaluation of risks based on personal experiences and what is seemingly obvious. Unfortunately, we are not common folks (thankfully so), so what we think is obvious may not be to the people we need to authroize funding for our program. Labeling an issue as "unsafe" is weak ground from which to fight when asking for large sums of money.

In an SMS, we need to use real information to assess risk and then prioritize safety issues based on pre-determined levels of what we are willing to accept and what we are not. Crosson offers eye opening factual information, and we must arm ourselves with numbers, not opinions, and attack serious safety issues from solid ground.

I am not a big fan of addressing every new hazard with a new policy. It frustrates me when I see this happen within government because often the policy is either not well thought out, or the wrong solution altogether. I also believe the bigger the policy manual gets, the less likely it is to be read or understood. Sometimes, however, a policy is a reasonable method of mitigating risk.

How many policies have you rolled your eyes at because the issuing authority failed to establish either probability or severity? Kneejerk policy to far-fetched or undocumented fears will doom a safety program and the credibility of management.

The nature of safety threats encourages self-policing to a fault. The very effects of the hazard diminish our ability to assess the associated risk level in real-time. It is similar to asking intoxicated people to evaluate their own level of impairment. In these cases, a policy created in an atmosphere of informed fact can protect us from our own limitations.

As long as there is need to protect our communities from the air, people will be at the core of airborne law enforcement operations. Risks associated with human factors will be an inescapable part of that activity. It is our responsibility to minimize risks as much as reasonably possible. For these reasons, aeromedical science must constantly be an integral part of our safety efforts. This means bringing quality research and science into everything we do.

ACTIONS CREATE REACTIONS

When an emergency starts, the time for analytical thought ends. Most people would agree that conditions such as stress, time limitations, uncertain goals and/or dynamic elements do not allow for analytical problem solving. However, many of our emergency procedures and much of the training designed to back up those procedures fail to take into account this fact.

In most critical incidents, such as an inflight emergency, we are left with intuitive processes, such as "naturalistic decision making." Under this broad category, we can process limited information under challenging conditions a number of different ways. Decisions can be made by selecting from multiple choices, responding with a conditioned rule-based response (i.e. "if this happens, I do this") or making creative choices based on experience, training and assumptions.

The theory of "recognition-primed decision making" says we can make quick decisions using limited information by comparing what information we have to certain patterns we have learned through training or experience. By associating current information to a known pattern, we can estimate the conclusion and make an appropriate decision. I like to think of this model as the "Wheel of Fortune" method. As you watch the letters slowly revealed in a Wheel of Fortune puzzle, your brain attempts to fit the clues available into a known word or phrase. At some point, you suddenly fit the clues into the formula and immediately advance to a conclusion. The better you are at connecting the clues to the pattern, the fewer clues you need.

Research in critical incident decision-making has shown that people who do well in stressful situations typically do not spend time formulating multiple alternatives and contemplating which would lead to the best result. Rather, they focus on collecting information to be used as cues, which can help connect the situation to a known pattern. That known pattern can then be used to guide the course of action needed, even if the situation is not yet fully understood. General Colin Powel said that, in combat, one should act on a plan when the probability of being successful is only 40-70 percent, because by the time 100 percent assurance is obtained, it is too late.

Making good decisions in a stressful environment relies on one critical component: situational awareness. To get to the right decision, we need to identify these cues and understand what they mean now and how they will influence our immediate future. When we look at accidents, we often talk about the person's inappropriate action (or inaction) and determine the solution is to practice the physical skill more. However, poor decision-making errors actually are more often a result of failures on the situational awareness side of the process rather than the improper selection or application of the physical action.

Colonel John Boyd invented the now famous OODA Loop concept in the 1960s. The model, "observe-orient-decide-act," explains the process required for decision-making. His application of the theory was to understand how an enemy makes decisions so the process could be interrupted and exploited. However, it also helps us understand how we can get to the correct "act" stage of the loop as well.

Again, we see the critical importance of situational awareness. The first two steps of the OODA Loop require that we observe the information available to us, identify the cues embedded in that information and orient ourselves accordingly.
Researchers have noted the best indicator of expert decision-making is not necessarily the performance of a maneuver, but superior awareness and assessment of situations, which allows the individual to select and perform the correct response at the right time.

How can we improve our situational awareness? Some of the most powerful methods are scenario-based training and maintaining our health and crew resource management. Despite it seeming obvious, we all need to be constantly reminded to maintain our health. Often, we base our physiological state on our ability to physically do a task. We do not admit to being fatigued, sick, dehydrated, hungry or mentally stressed until we fail to do something at the proficiency level we expect of ourselves. For example, have you ever pushed yourself while driving fatigued until you caught yourself drifting out of your lane?

Until that moment, we all believe we are in control of our substandard state. The fact is these factors erode the ability to observe, process and understand information long before the point we notice our physical abilities have degraded.

Even when we are mentally and physically at peak performance, natural human limitations inhibit our ability to take in all the information available to us. In 1950, Alex Varney wrote in *The Psychology of Flight*, "The lives of good men, and the success of an engagement, depend on the actions of other men." Training in crew resource management can augment the situational awareness a single person can obtain on their own, filling in critical missing cues that can be used for pattern recognition.

Perception is based on changes. To recognize the status of something has changed, we must be aware of the former, or typical, state. This conflicts with the fact that constant vigilance is impossible in a complex environment with numerous items that require monitoring, such as the cockpit of a public safety aircraft during a mission. We simply cannot look at everything 100 percent of the time. Changes in the status of the aircraft or systems can slip by undetected if the change is not obvious or rapid.

During a critical incident, stress, tunnel vision and information overload can severely limit a person's ability to monitor everything, letting some changes go unnoticed. Such undetectable changes can draw an airplane into a stall/spin situation, cause attitude deviations while flying in instrument conditions or allow an engine problem to slowly progress. Adding a second set of eyes and ears to the monitoring process can inhibit these sneaky deviations by overlapping the scan of the other person.

None of this information can benefit us unless we incorporate it into our training. Safety officers and instructors need to work together to identify the most likely scenarios in which a hazard will likely try to bite us. By understanding the scenario, we can identify the available cues and likely decision-making processes that will be available to the people we are training. Those cues are critical to proper decision making because they are needed for situational awareness.

Scenario-based training establishes the patterns we will reference in critical situations when information is scarce and stress abundant. We also need to determine what anomalies may come up during a particular scenario that would change the pattern and chain of actions required of the crew.

One of the advantages of intuitive decision-making versus analytical decision-making is the fact that we can quickly close the OODA Loop with immediate feedback. Our actions create reactions in our environment that we can observe and orient ourselves to before continuing to the next decision. To perform this skill in fluid and stressful situations requires specific training.

Training to perform a specific maneuver or action is important, but it is not enough. We also need to practice recognizing when and why to apply the actions we have practiced. If we look at accidents related to engine failures, we will find far too many that were aggravated not by the inability of the pilot to perform an "engine out" maneuver, but in the pilot's delayed application of the procedure or flat out failure to initiate the procedure at all.

When designing any normal or emergency procedure, back it up with education and realistic training. The value of the education we receive from reading accident reports, magazine articles, textbooks, attending classes or sharing stories cannot be underestimated. It helps increase our database of decision-making cues. But to ensure success, we need experience in reading a situation and performing a task, not simply talking or reading about it.

I used to sit with my grandmother and watch Wheel of Fortune. I am ashamed to admit it, but it was a bit of a competition and I tried hard to win against that little old lady. Still, she would beat me nearly 100 percent of the time. Grandma watched a lot of Wheel of Fortune, and no college degree I had could compete with that experience.

ADDING LAYERS OF SAFETY

Growing up in Minnesota, the harsh winters required adherence to a few universal rules for survival. Always expect a snowball ambush at the bus stop, don't lick metal signposts no matter how much money you are offered, and dress in layers. No matter how warm any sweater, jacket or thermal underwear was, it was never good enough by itself. Safety is like that.

When we are presented with a safety issue, we go through the process of analyzing the hazard and associated risk, discussing it with our safety committee and developing an effective risk control. These controls can involve training, procedure changes, equipment purchases, etc. We expect a risk control that comes out of such a formal process to be effective—if we take the time to follow a well thought-out method of designing the safety measure, it usually will be successful. However, even the most successful risk control will not be 100 percent effective in controlling the risk it is designed to attack.

If we assume perfect reliability for any safety measure is 1 (or 100 percent), the actual probability of success is 1 minus the probability of failure. So what is the probability of failure? This is a question that several industries have tried to answer with engineering and statistics since the U.S. military developed MIL-Q-9858, the first quality control standard, in 1959.

The electronics manufacturing industry and NASA were some of the first to attempt quantification and prediction of failures in component production and life limits in the 1960s. By the 1980s, automobile makers, aerospace and industrial manufacturing had embraced these concepts through programs such as ISO 9000. In the early 2000s, operational safety folks began to experiment in using these component reliability-engineering methods to address human factors and operational safety issues. These ideas led to many of the components that eventually became safety management systems.

However, the application of safety engineering to operational safety is not as effective as one might hope. Many of the academic methods of predicting probability of failure are based on relatively controlled environments. Factories and engineered components involve variables that can be more readily predicted than the operational use of those parts and machines in the real world by human beings.

Even under Six Sigma, the strict, renowned quality control method developed by Motorola in 1986, the best users can hope for is 3.4 defective parts per million, or 99 percent reliability. According to one report, the medical industry averages only 55 percent reliability that a new drug being tested will be effective and safe.

In Advisory Circular 25.1309-1A, *System Design and Analysis*, FAA says a failure is "improbable" if it is predicted to occur 1 in 100,000 to 1 in 1 billion times. In our dynamic public safety aviation world, we could never hope to achieve such high reliability predictions. Even if we could, a 1 percent chance still means failure is likely to happen at some point. God may be my copilot, but Murphy and his book of laws are always in the back seat waiting for his opportunity to capitalize on "improbabilities."

The famous United Airlines flight 232 crash in Sioux City, IA, is discussed in almost every crew resource management course, and for good reason. In that accident, the crew had to respond to a hydraulics failure scenario that was deemed to have an "extremely remote" probability of occurring by even the NTSB (Report# AAR-90/06). In other words, there was less than a 1 percent probability of failure.

What is an aviator to do? First, instead of brain numbing calculus equations to determine probability of failure, let's look at determining the probability of success in a proposed risk control. The APSA *SMS Installation Guide* contains a hazard-tracking log that includes a probability of success calculation page. The process involves asking questions about the funding and personnel available for a proposed safety control.

It also asks about the prior experience those involved have in implementing a similar plan, how closely related the control is to the risk,
etc. By answering 11 simple questions, we can estimate the probability
of success.

Some of us are perfectionists and will tinker with a plan, collecting
information and adjusting, trying to get as close to 100 percent reliability as possible. Others are naysayers, pointing out the imperfections in
any risk control as reason to disregard the plan. Do not get bogged
down in developing safety controls that have 100 percent reliability.
Retired General Colin Powell once recommended moving forward with a
plan if you have 40-70 percent probability of success. He suggested that
waiting until the plan was assured success usually meant you would miss
the opportunity. While 40 percent, in my opinion, is a little too low for
aviation safety, 70 percent is not unreasonable.

Accept that you will not have 100 percent reliability, and plan for
it. The FAA *Advisory Circular* mentioned states that, "In any system or
subsystem, the failure of any single element, component or connection during any one flight should be assumed, regardless of its probability. Such single failures should not prevent continued safe flight and
landing or significantly reduce the capability of the airplane or...crew
to cope with the resulting failure conditions." This philosophy is used
by our aircraft manufacturers to deliver extremely complex, yet reliable products. We can use the same approach in our safety management. Develop layers of safety controls that together can offer better
results than any one plan could.

When NASA launched Apollo XI to the moon, the mission only had an
86 percent probability of success. Some of the astronauts famously gave
it a 50/50 chance of making it to the surface of the moon. During the
final minutes of descent, the computer on the lander failed, requiring
Neil Armstrong and Buzz Aldrin to engage the secondary system, the
manual controls. They successfully hand flew the spacecraft to the surface, though they were not near the intended landing spot. The need
for manual controls was debated during the design of early spacecraft

and only put in reluctantly as a backup to the computer. That secondary level of safety also saved Alan Shephard, who needed to manually adjust Freedom 7's alignment for reentry during his historic flight.

In the United Airlines flight 232 accident, 185 of the 296 people on board survived due to the effectiveness of a secondary safety layer— the crew. A reliable layering of safety using both physical component engineering and human performance can be effective. Design the aircraft as best as possible, then train the aircrews to deal with the remote possibilities that cannot be completely designed out. We also see manufacturers including multiple system-design layers, i.e. redundant systems or backups.

When we sit in our safety committee meetings deciding how to address an identified hazard, we need to consider implementing at least two risk controls. This may mean a physical barrier, such as a piece of gear or limiting device, and a policy or procedure to direct human action.

For example, to mitigate tools being left in an aircraft, you may have a physical tool control system (shadow box, electronic tool tracking, etc.) and a quality control procedure to have a second person check the aircraft using a checklist after maintenance is complete. Both safety measures by themselves have a high probability of success but are not 100 percent reliable. Together, they complement each other and work far better than either could alone.

Stall/spin risk might be attacked through the installation of an angle of attack indicator and a change in flight profile (altitude and airspeed) or aircrew training.

Risk is a product of both the likelihood of an incident occurring and the severity of that incident should it occur. These two components offer us two layers of safety management. For example, with bird strikes, a means of decreasing likelihood may be avoiding certain areas of high bird concentration (e.g. landfills) or using aircraft pulse lighting. To reduce the severity of a bird strike, we can use helmets and visors or polycarbonate canopies.

You may decide to mitigate weather related risks by upgrading avionics or getting instrument training for pilots to minimize the severity of unplanned entry into IMC. To lower the likelihood of entering such conditions in the first place, you could also train flight crews on enroute decision points and address them in your FRAT. Again, two options with less than 100 percent reliability together offer a much higher probability of success.

Any safety layer we put in place will not be perfect. We cannot place all our hopes for a safe operation in any one item. But that is not a reason to abandon any of the risk controls we come up with. If we have a reasonably high probability of success, put it into action along with another risk control. If all you can come up with are ideas that have lower probability of success estimates, try out two or three.

We do not want to bog down operations with ineffective risk controls, so balance the plan with realistic predictions of reliability. If one of your safety layers involves equipment, think of a second that involves human factors. A plan to control the likelihood of an incident should be complemented with a strategy to reduce the severity of the same incident if we fail to prevent it.

In Minnesota, wanting to be warm while walking to the bus stop in January had no impact on how cold I felt. Wearing my best winter jacket did not keep snowballs from finding the exposed part of my neck when the battle began. But when hunting, a pair of gloves inside a giant pair of mittens kept my fingers from freezing up in the deer stand at sunrise.

To keep warm, I had to dress in layers. Safety is not a result of good intentions, it is a product of actually doing things right. It is a goal that can only be reached through a thoughtful process that leaves all vulnerabilities covered by interwoven layers of protection. Without it, our fate is left exposed to the elements.

SAFETY HAS NEW TOOLS, NEW CHALLENGES

"There are no new ways to crash an aircraft." While a true statement, I find it more useful to consider the idea that "there are new ways to keep aircraft from crashing." I see more and more of these "new" means of achieving aviation safety every year. Increasingly, technology plays a vital role in these new safety tools and methods.

One goal of a safety management system (SMS) is to make meaningful and effective safety decisions. We can think of it as cutting away the safety "fat." An SMS needs to address real, not assumed, risks with programs that can be tracked so their effectiveness is known instead of presumed. Doing this requires information. The safety officer needs to use data generated by hazard reports, inspections, incident analysis, flight risk assessment scores, maintenance trends and as many other sources as possible. The more data, the more effective the program can be.

Using traditional methods, a safety officer can set up this process in a basic manner. Simple documents and spreadsheets help to gather and record required information. Sometimes, maintenance tracking or pilot records can be helpful in accessing useful data. In the end, however, the safety officer usually is left with a labor-intensive process of manually compiling information and entering it into databases or filing systems. Safety officers are also required to analyze the information in a manner that will allow them to see the trends and indicators they need to address with their SMS. Even in this basic format, such an SMS is already a big step beyond the traditional safety program, which is typically driven by a "whack-a-mole" strategy of dealing with problems as they arise.

Ultimately, there is too much information for one person to collect and manage manually. This is especially true in the law enforcement industry where the safety officer is usually also covering a shift as a flight crewmember, instructor, maintenance assistant, crime analyst and cleaning staff. If we are truly committed to safety, we must provide safety officers with the training and resources they need to do the best job possible. A logical step is to use a software package that can take the data management process to the next level. Such computer-based solutions not only improve the collection and analysis of critical information, but also streamline communications in the rest of the unit and simplify SMS performance monitoring.

Let's take the example of a flight risk assessment tool (FRAT). The purpose of a FRAT is to identify the risks involved in a flight and offer an avenue for mitigating them. This information is extremely useful to the safety officer. Over time, the categories that frequently score high on a FRAT can be used by the safety officer to develop risk mitigations, such as training, equipment maintenance or improved procedures. FRAT information shows real risks effecting operations on a regular basis. By lowering these risks, the safety program can not only lower risk but also increase operational availability by removing some of the roadblocks to responding to calls. This is the perfect example of how an SMS should work.

However, compiling all individual FRAT scores for each flight crew takes time. Even in a simple scenario where a unit has two flight crews per day covering 12-hour shifts, the safety officer would need to record the scores of a minimum of 730 FRATs per year. This is just one source of data the safety officer should be looking at. Add these hundreds of FRAT scores to the hazard reports, equipment squawks, inspection items, HUMS/HFDM data and dozens of other information sources in the safety officer's files, and something will have to give. Most likely, your unit will simply be missing out on opportunities to improve safety and operational efficiency.

How do people in your unit make anonymous safety reports about hazards or incidents? Many of us use a simple "drop box" because even email can be traced. Once a report is made, how is it stored? Where are the associated follow-up documents the safety officer fills out? How is feedback given to the reporting person, especially when anonymous? How are these reports and follow-up actions made known to other unit members? These simple reporting and communications challenges can be headaches for a safety officer. Simple word processor programs and emails offer solutions that again require precious time and effort to utilize. An automated system can streamline this process and free up the safety officer to do tasks that are more meaningful than hammering away at a keyboard for hours on end.

As I said, the more data we have, the more effective our SMS can be. However, just because we have data or the means of collecting data does not guarantee the program will produce a safer operation. The safety officer needs to be able to understand the information and how to use it. This is not an intuitive skill; it takes training. Buying the necessary equipment and not sending a safety officer for training is like buying a new WAAS-capable GPS, giving it to student pilots and expecting them to shoot an approach to minimums.

Not only does the safety officer need training, but management does as well. From a manager's point of view, the safety officer will be bringing new, exciting sources of information to the operation. It is critical that bosses use the information in a manner that will promote safety. There will be a temptation to make grand, knee-jerk reactions or use the information to punish employees that get "caught." Flight data monitoring information is a common example of how this process can go wrong. When the safety program generates risk information based on how an aircraft is being flown, the goal must remain focused on what can be done to mitigate the risk. If FRAT information shows a trend in fatigue, how can the unit minimize those occurrences? Is it a problem with an individual or the system? Does "just culture" apply? Slapping an individual in the face with a bunch of data will not likely improve your

> "Computer-based solutions not only improve the collection and analysis of critical information, but also streamline communications with the rest of the unit and simplify SMS performance monitoring."

RISK DESCRIPTION	RESPONSE		C
Captain with less than 200 hours in type	No	Yes	
First Officer with less than 200 hours in type	No	Yes	
Single Pilot Flight	No	Yes	
Captain with less than 100 hours last 90 days	No	Yes	
First Officer with less than 100 hours in last 90 days	No	Yes	
Duty day greater than 12 hours	No	Yes	
Flight time (Greater than 8 hours in the duty day)	No	Yes	
Crew Rest (Less than 10 hours prior to the duty day)	No	Yes	
engineer with less 5years experience	No	Yes	

NOTE: Please note that Risk Values can only be reset to 'NO' if there are comments

employee's chances of getting home safely after each shift. Such actions will likely result in decreased participation in the safety program.

To ensure participation in the program, the entire unit must be trained in how to interact with an SMS, especially as it becomes more technical. How do they enter data? What will the information be used for? What does the information mean to them and their ability to do their job better? Ultimately, this is the key to making an SMS, especially a robust one with advanced tools, successful. Some tools can remove an element of human error from the data collection process, such as FRATs that automatically import weather, flight crew, location and mainte-nance information. No matter how automated we make the SMS, how-ever, some of the most crucial data will still need to be entered by people. Furthermore, that information will need to be understood by people and, in the end, utilized by people. These critical obstacles can only be addressed with training for every member of the unit. If the in-formation isn't entered accurately, or if people don't follow the safety recommendations, all of these systems are useless.

Still, as tempting as it may be to add all of the new bells and whistles to your SMS as soon as possible, pace yourself. Trying to do it all at once has been one of the greatest failures of SMS implementation over the last decade. Take it one small step at a time. This will give the safety officer time to properly implement each element and make changes as needed. It will also let the unit get used to these changes in a manner that minimizes any negative impact on operations. A paced, methodical implementation process will help unit members accept and participate in the new safety management processes.

SMS are not created to serve the safety program or generate data. An SMS is about people and the system they work within. Our data and new tools must always remain focused on that.

STAYING VIGILANT:
Survey Indicates Complacency Ranks
High Among Safety Concerns

Complacency in public safety aviation is always near the top of the list of safety concerns. In both the 2016 and 2017 safety surveys APSA conducted, complacency made it into the top 5 issues members listed as the most significant threats to our safety. The other four items were IIMC, training, fatigue and maintenance/mechanical failures. It could be argued complacency plays a significant role in all four other major concerns.

Despite its prevalence, complacency is a difficult safety issue to address. Often, we are left telling ourselves, "Hey, complacency is bad, so don't be complacent." Heck, I'm sure some version of those words have left my mouth more than once. Yet, I know I am a prime suspect for complacency. I've been flying the same make and model aircraft for eight years, doing basically the same job, sometimes for years with the same flight crew.

The last time the National Transportation Safety Board looked at pilots involved in public use category accidents, they found the average flight time was 3,500-4,500 hours, depending on the aircraft category. I fall into this range, too. And I have caught myself having temporary attacks of complacency. However, it has always been after the fact, as I believe is the case for most people. I have never met a pilot or mechanic who said, "Dang, I think I'm being a bit complacent today. I should do something about it."

We need to know how to monitor ourselves and fix complacency before it bites us. Telling ourselves to be careful is not enough. We have to understand the problem before we can talk about fixing it.

Complacency is defined as: 1) Self-satisfaction, especially when accompanied by unawareness of actual dangers or deficiencies, and 2) an instance of usually unaware or uninformed self-satisfaction.

I asked the APSA online safety officer group how they would define complacency as well. Here are some of their responses:

- Feeling secure while unaware of potential danger because of misperception of risk or increased risk tolerance.
- Standardized deviation from normal practices due to lack of negative historical consequences.
- Expectation of a planned result with little thought of needing an alternate plan.
- Performing an act or procedure so often that one starts to believe no mistakes could or would ever be made.
- Recognizing no need to improve or learn because you've always done it a certain way and never had an accident.

Some common themes in these definitions are an expectation for things to work out, an expected outcome and degraded awareness. This condition can lead to degraded work performance and a lack of attention to detail, which turns into errors and mistakes. Like many safety issues, the effects of complacency start small and build slowly over time, making the problem difficult to detect until it is too late. We have to know we are being complacent before we can correct it.

As a professional aviator, I try to maintain a level of expertise that will ensure a successful outcome of any activity I engage in. But how can I tell when I am being confident or moving into complacency? The first red flag of complacency to consider is training. I once heard someone say it takes a bit more than a lifetime to learn everything about aviation. The idea is that there is always something more that we need to learn or some skill that could be improved.

The "continuous improvement" management model was developed at AT&T in the 1920s. One of the fundamental assumptions of the model is that things can only be in one of two states: moving forward or moving backward. Sometimes we feel we have reached a plateau where we have heard it all. Perhaps we feel we are not getting anything new out of training. We find ourselves saying, "I've done this training 100 times and don't really need to do it again."

Our skills in aviation are perishable. This is true for pilots, mechanics, flight officers, medics and so on. No matter how many years we've been in the industry, how many classes we've attended or how many articles we've read, if we are not moving forward, we are moving backward. Training, learning, reviewing and practicing are how we stay moving in the right direction.

While new and advanced skills are often what we crave, reviewing the basics of our profession is a critical step in fighting complacency. As Bruce Lee said, "Advanced skills are the basics mastered," adding that, "I fear not the man who has practiced 10,000 kicks once, but I fear the man who has practiced one kick 10,000 times."

We must take a look at ourselves and ask when was the last time we opened a textbook, participated in a training event, or watched an online class or webinar. We cannot always count on our employer to arrange training for us. We can each do a lot on our own. The more we train, the less complacent we will be. It is not just the knowledge, but the process of staying fresh and moving forward that protects us from falling backwards.

The next red flag is participation in safety efforts. What have you done to identify hazards and fix them? When was the last time you filled out a safety or hazard report for the safety manager because you noticed something could be improved? Have you ever done it? None of our operations are perfect. There is always room for improvement. Failing to identify or address the hazards in our operations feeds into complacency.

The third red flag is addiction to routine. Sure, having a workflow for certain tasks is important. However, if your daily activities are so structured you become uncomfortable or even angry if something interferes with the routine, you should be concerned. Often, we use routine as a crutch for true proficiency. It also locks us into a stagnant awareness of our surroundings, which in reality are in a constant state of change. We will not see or choose to ignore those changes for love of our routine.

Our attitudes about our job influence our motivation, which drives performance. Regarding the "Theory of Planned Behavior," psychologists Ariane Colémont and Stephan Van den Broucke state a strong connection exists between individual safety behavior and attitudes. This seems like common sense, but Colémont and Van den Broucke have also found the actual controls put in place to impact our behavior have minimal discernable influence. Much to the dismay of our bosses, telling us what to do does not guide behavior as much as our attitudes. This is because attitude creates the culture of an organization and its operations.

Our commitment to the organization impacts these attitudes. In the 1991 work "The Three Component Model of Commitment," John Meyer and Natalie Allen break down our motivations into three categories. The most traditional is the sense of obligation to an employer. Next is a fear of losing a job, either because of financial loss or career damage. Neither of these two motivations are healthy and often lead to complacency.

The third motivation is affection for your job. This is how we often enter into the aviation and public safety worlds. We do our job because we love it. This passion translates into motivation, which is a deterrent to complacency. Over time, though, we start to fade toward a feeling of our job being a paycheck. Ask yourself why you do what you do. If your answer leans heavily toward fear of loss and/or obligation, realize the stage is set for complacency to steal the show.

I believe we are all complacent at some level. If we want to fight complacency before it hits us in our blind spots, we must start by accepting it exists in us and around us. Looking for the consequences of complacency, such as errors and mistakes, is joining the fight after blood has been drawn. In a preemptive attack, we must look at training and participation in safety programs, as well as our routines and feelings about our job. These few items constitute a health check and offer remedies.

The solution is to attack complacency every day—to continuously seek out where it is corroding our operation and chase it off. This is not something that will work if we just do it once in a while. The simple fact is, we can only be moving forward or backward. If we are not doing something to improve ourselves, we are allowing complacency to drag us back until we stumble and fall.

COMMON DISTRACTIONS:
Staying Focused on the Ground and In Flight

What are the common distractions we face during the different phases of our day as public safety aviators? The question was asked during a recent APSA safety officer meeting, and the answers we came up with were interesting in two ways. First, some common distractions showed up on most peoples' lists. Second and more unsettling to me, people mentioned numerous valid distractions I had not taken into account.

What distractions do we face during preflight? The most common distractions we considered involved conversation with coworkers, supervisors and visitors, as well as mail/package delivery. Conversation distractions can be electronic, such as from the dispatch radio, computer messages and cell phones.

The environment was mentioned by a number of safety officers. The distractions include air temperature, precipitation, facility neatness and aircraft noise. Three people suggesting becoming greasy, dirty or overly sweaty during preflight can be enough of a distraction to lower preflight quality.

Personal problems at home were on one person's list. Problems with coworkers and supervisors were mentioned by another.

Conversations, including electronic exchanges, were the most prevalent distraction suggested during startup. The scope of the conversations, however, extended to mission-related dialogue about the flight initiated by passengers or ATC. Unusual aircraft noises, instrument indications or activity on the ramp, such as pedestrians, other aircraft or wildlife, were also added to the list. Two people mentioned similar distractions when leaving a static display in front of a crowd of people.

During takeoff, conversation again came up as a leading distraction. Interesting distractions mentioned by several people were changes in tasking from ATC, dispatch or ground units requesting assistance. Some members also brought up tasking changes forced on the crew by unanticipated weather, air traffic, birds or aircraft issues, which can distract a flight crew from other essential tasks.

The longest list of distractions was found during actual calls or missions. Communication distractions were epidemic in this phase. Bombardment from ATC, dispatch, ground units, aircrew members, ATC and other air traffic were added to aircraft instruments, navigation and airframe noise. The environment came back up, with temperature, noise, vibration, sunlight, darkness and motion adding to the bucket of distractions. The mission itself was one of the most significant threats on the list. Information ambiguity and confusion was an all-too-common distractor.

We work in some of the most interesting conditions in the world when we are on a mission. They make movies about what we are looking at out the window and through our cameras. The pull on our attention is undeniable.

An often-overlooked phase of flight is returning to base. According to studies, this is one of the highest risk phases of flight, especially if we are returning due to worsening weather, low fuel or human-related pressures like maximum bladder capacity or hunger. The distractions presented by "letting down" too much after a mission but before landing were mentioned by several group members. The frustration, heartache or jubilation created by the mission itself also can be a massive distraction, especially if we combine it with premature relaxation.

The feelings stirred up by a successful or unsuccessful flight spilled over onto the distraction list for post-flight activity. Depending on how the mission went, we may lose ourselves in rerunning the flight in our heads before our post-flight chores are done.

Communication distractions in this phase came from phone calls and messages from ground units, dispatch and supervisors, which sometimes start before we get out of the aircraft. The human needs-related distractions become stronger than ever once the restroom or refrigerator are within striking distance.

It may seem like a low-risk time to worry about distractions, but plenty can go wrong if we allow our attention to be pulled from our tasking too early after a flight. I personally believe post-flight distractions keep the replacement fuel cap industry in business. And many of us have forgotten to write up a maintenance squawk or return equipment after a flight due to distractions. The fatigue that often sets in after a long flight also increases the power of distractions.

Several distractions spanned all operations, from beginning to end. Cell phones were the most prominent. Also mentioned were things like supervisor pressure, budget concerns, personal life issues and changes in schedule. My favorite item under this category was "stupid people."

The maintenance side of our profession is equally plagued by the dangers of distractions. The FAA's "Dirty Dozen" list of common maintenance-related human factors includes distractions, and for good reason. Several high-profile accidents have been attributed to distractions during aircraft maintenance.

Conversation, including on cell phones, is at the top of this list, as well. Uncomfortable climate, noise and additional activity not associated with the task at hand all add to the list of distractions in the maintenance bay.

With all these distractions to consider, the question is, "What can we do about it?" We have two options. First, we can mitigate or remove many distractions. Second, we can expect the impact of the distractions we cannot remove and learn how to deal with them.

The FAA addressed unnecessary conversation in 1981 when it developed the sterile cockpit concept. The idea works well for the structured atmosphere of airline transport. But public safety aviators are rarely in "cruise" flight, the only phase allowing for cockpit conversation if you are following FAA guidelines.

The expectation of flying for hours without talking to the other person in the cockpit about anything non-critical is unreasonable. However, we can recognize certain phases of flight when we should hold the conversation about fishing last weekend. Under the FAA's sterile cockpit concept, non-essential conversation is limited during takeoff and landing below 10,000 feet. For most of us, we are transitioning to "en route" at 1,000 feet or below. Beyond takeoff, many of us work in a completely unscripted environment. Other than the inevitable landing at the end of the flight, we cannot predict where we will be going, what we will be doing there, or for how long.

We can, however, rely on change. We can expect a change in mission tasking as well as in location or direction of travel. The weather often changes; ATC may change routing or clearances. The aircraft may change how it decides to behave, or the aircrew may change in health, fatigue or stress. All of the changes mark a time when distractions can impede our ability to gather the information we need and make a proper decision about what to do next. These are times when a sterile cockpit rule should be employed.

Sterile cockpit techniques do not mean no talking is allowed. They mean only essential conversation should be taking place. This is a crew resource management skill. CRM is not just for emergencies; it is for the entire day at work, both in and out of the cockpit. Knowing when and how to communicate effectively in the aircraft or maintenance bay will cut the fat out of communication when we have constraints on time or human performance.

We cannot fix something unless we identify it first. We all need to recognize distractions from electronic devices, such as cell phones, tablets, mission systems and avionics, are a problem. However, removing them from our operations is not easy. A ban on cell phones or tablets fails to take into account how they are used for modern public safety operations.

In 2014, FAA published the *Prohibition on Personal Use of Electronic Devices on the Flight Deck* rule. Despite the title, the administration did not ban personal devices from the flight deck. It simply required they be used for essential flight tasks. If we bring our cell phones or tablets into the cockpit or maintenance bay, we must limit their use to the functions that assist our operation. We must identify what we are going to use them for and when. During the critical phases of flight, they should be limited, unless they are being used to deal with a change at hand. During takeoff and landing, they should be stowed. Facebook is not a critical flight function, no matter how sweet the sunset photo from 2,000 feet.

Despite our best efforts, distractions will eventually cause us to miss or mess up an important task. There is no avoiding the eventuality of human error.

> "What we need to remember is the checklist is not there to remind us how to operate an aircraft we are already familiar with; it is there to mitigate the mistakes that are created by distractions."

Checklists are sometimes seen by aircrews as uncool tools used by rookies who do not know the aircraft well. But more of us should use them. Granted, many checklists are poorly designed. What we need to remember is the checklist is not there to remind us how to operate an aircraft with which we are familiar. It is there to mitigate the mistakes created by distractions—that 0.1 percent of the time a distraction can make us fail to flip a switch. Checklists are simple and effective tools for complex and unpredictable problems.

When all else fails, move back two steps. Recognize the distractions in your workplace and react to them when they occur. Be suspicious they have caused a potentially damaging situation and take a moment to gain perspective. The rule of thumb is to go back two steps before the distraction and make sure you didn't miss anything. This can be more difficult to do in flight, but that is where good CRM comes into play.

SITUATIONAL ENLIGHTENMENT:
Trained TFOs Make A Difference

"I'm the guy who keeps your son out of trouble" was how one of my TFOs introduced himself to my mother. We all laughed, but he was absolutely right. There has been no shortage of articles on the impact a trained tactical flight officer can have on the effectiveness of law enforcement aviation. When it comes to completing missions successfully, nothing is more potent than TFO selection and training.

I have had the pleasure of working with some true professionals whose mastery of tactics and mission equipment qualifies as high art. Such a level of expertise only comes from training, dedication and experience. What has not been discussed as much is the impact a professional TFO can have on flight safety. On a few occasions, I have had to put an aircraft on the ground at a time and place not of my choosing. The role my TFO played in each case made a great impact on my opinion of the significance TFOs play in flight safety.

But this was just my opinion, and as a proponent of safety management systems, I know opinion is not sufficient. I needed to look at the facts.

When one mentions TFO inclusion in flight safety training, crew resource management (CRM) immediately comes to mind. CRM is a broad topic addressing safety and accomplishment of the goals of a flight. One of the aspects of CRM that can be universally applied to any operation is its impact on situational awareness (SA). Loss of SA is one of the leading causes of human error related accidents and, as we know, human error is consistently the leading contributing factor in accidents. A International Helicopter Safety Team report lists "pilot judgment and actions" as a causal factor in 84 percent of the helicopter accidents analyzed. The team has identified "pilot situational awareness" as an issue in 31 percent of those same cases. These numbers come as no surprise.

A leading cause of fatalities in law enforcement aviation is inadvertent flight into instrument meteorological conditions (ending in CFIT). We also consistently have leading accident categories related to stall/spin, training and loss of control. Eroded SA plays a role in all these categories.

Another top accident category in law enforcement aviation is aircraft component failures. Anyone who has experienced a mechanical issue in flight can attest to how fast SA can slip away from a pilot trying to understand what has happened, apply the proper corrective action and continue to fly the aircraft.

Obviously, maintaining SA has a monumental influence on flight safety in our business. According to aviation human factors expert Harry Orlady, SA can be lost three ways: 1) Failure to correctly perceive the situation. 2) Failure to comprehend the situation. Or, 3) Failure to comprehend the situation in the future.

Studies have shown that over 80 percent of loss of SA incidents can be attributed to the first factor, failure to correctly perceive the situation. This can come from distractions, inadequate training, information processing errors, etc. Many of these issues are common to law enforcement pilots during missions. With new equipment added to our already dynamic operations, there is often more information in the cockpit than one person can possibly process at once.

Again, if tasks cannot be separated between crewmembers, something has to give and some information will be ignored. Unfortunately, an experienced pilot will often be inclined to ignore the information he or she is most experienced with. However, studies have shown the ignored material is often critical to safety. In law enforcement, the effect can be aggravated by the fact that the situation on the ground can be considerably more interesting than the oil pressure gauge that has not moved in over an hour.

The loss of SA due to a failure to correctly perceive the situation can come from ambiguity between two pieces of information, as well. When we suddenly are unable to straighten out the inconsistency between two pieces of information, SA can feel as if it is suspended. You have lost orientation in the world around you, and you know it, but you cannot figure out how to take hold of reality again. This situation can actually lead to vertigo and panic, which amplifies the problem.

A trained TFO can stop loss of SA quickly and easily through basic CRM tactics. First, a competent TFO can run a mission without assistance from the pilot other than aircraft placement. Sure, a pilot can add valuable assistance to the TFO during a call; however, this must always be a secondary task. When the need arises to concentrate on flying, the lure of diverting precious attention to the call is erased with a TFO on board. By having a trained TFO who can run the call without assistance, the division of tasks is defined. This division keeps the pilot primarily focused on the information needed to maintain SA. If the pilot is preoccupied helping a TFO who cannot run mission equipment or manage ground resources, flight responsibilities begin to fade into the background, where they can change without the pilot's knowledge, slowly eroding SA.

Sometimes, confirming information or pointing something out that has gone unprocessed will snap the pilot back into SA. Often, this simple verbal confirmation of perspective on incorrectly processed information can be the thing that breaks the accident chain. The second category, failure to comprehend the situation, accounts for 17 percent of loss of SA incidents. The pilot may not even know he or she has lost SA, and a simple, "What are you doing?" or, "Where are we going?" can regain it. Flight instructors do this constantly to help us keep our head wrapped around a situation: "Check your airspeed," "Watch your descent rate," or "Where is the CDI pointing?" These comments are usually followed by some sort of unintelligible grunt from the pilot and, hopefully, corrective action. That brief eureka moment, when you realize something was going wrong without your knowledge, marks the return to SA. A trained TFO can offer the same situational enlightenment.

TFOs can also help process information when the volume of critical info exceeds what a pilot can reasonably take in. Emergency procedures are a good example of this. I experienced the need to perform an emergency landing on a busy road from 500 feet one day. My TFO assisted in confirming the location, checking for obstructions, calling out traffic on the roadway and communicating our situation and position over the radio. My tasks were reduced significantly, allowing me to concentrate on flying the aircraft to the designated spot.

So, loss of SA is a leading element in accidents in our business. A trained TFO can theoretically counter the main factors that can cause a pilot to lose SA. Do we have any data that backs up these theories?

The information is somewhat limited, but from 2011 through 2013, there were 34 law enforcement aviation accident cases with enough data on crew composition and causal factors to be helpful. Six of the incidents were during training with a flight instructor, so that brings us down to 28. System component failures, such as engine failures, were associated with nine accidents. It would be interesting to know if the TFO played a role in the outcome of each of these cases, but the reports do not have this info. This leaves us with 19 of the original 34 cases that are primarily human-error accidents during non-training flights.

Of the 19 human-error accidents, 15 occurred without a second trained crewmember. They were either conducted as single-pilot missions or without a trained TFO. This is 79 percent of the accidents. The non-TFO accidents accounted for 8 of the 11 fatalities (72 percent).

This means that for the four human-error accidents during normal operations with a TFO, 15 similar accidents occurred in aircraft without a second trained crewmember. I am not able to factor in total flight hours in each of the two categories. Since the majority of agencies currently use trained TFOs for normal ops, if we were to factor in flight hours in each category, I think it is reasonable to assume we would find the difference in accident rates even further apart.

Of the 15 accidents that occurred without a trained crewmember aboard, 12 resulted from factors that are included in the syllabus I use when training a new TFO. In other words, a trained TFO likely would have been equipped to identify and assist the pilot in avoiding or minimizing at least one major factor that lead to 80 percent of those accidents.

In SMS terms, we have a significant hazard to flight safety in the form of human error resulting from, at least partially, loss of SA. The 19 accidents and 11 fatalities our industry has suffered from these types of accidents in the last three years illustrate a high level of risk associated with this hazard. Research suggests that a trained crewmember, such as a TFO, would be an effective way to lower this risk. Furthermore, data from the last three years indicates there is a correlation between trained TFOs and a lower accident rate.

If you want an air unit that consistently completes missions success-fully and is known for saving lives and putting bad guys in jail, spend some time and effort training your TFOs. If you want a safe operation that has the lowest amount of risk possible and is ready to deal with any emergency so every employee has the best chance of surviving, spend some time and effort training your TFOs.

PLANNING FOR THE WORST:
Incident Response Plans Go Beyond Safety

When the TFO began to speak on his police radio, the Gainesville (FL) Police Department heard something they had never heard before. "Mayday, mayday, mayday," the TFO radioed. "Air-1 is going down behind Butler Plaza." Members of another aircrew were sitting at their desks in disbelief, waiting for the next transmission. A long 10 seconds of silence passed before they heard more. "Air-1 is down on the ground," the TFO said. Fortunately, the aircrew had come down safely. But what next? The next few minutes would either minimize further injury to personnel, the agency and the unit or amplify it.

Just as a police officer may go his or her whole career training with a firearm but never fire it in the line of duty, a chief pilot or safety officer may spend a whole career preparing the unit for an incident that will never occur. But once in a while, we are offered the opportunity to see if all the training, practice and program writing was actually worth the time and effort.

On Dec. 8, 2011, around 1630 hours, Richard Bray of the Alachua County (FL) Sheriff's Office and Juan DeCastro of the Gainesville (FL) Police Department, both members of the two departments' joint aviation unit, were 10 minutes into a patrol flight. DeCastro was a new TFO who had just completed his daytime training. While investigating a suspicious vehicle near a busy shopping complex, the aircrew's engine began to spool down. It was a partial power degradation, which has led many pilots to attempt to continue flight or troubleshoot instead of land. Bray did not make the same mistake. Safety training took over, and he started towards a nearby field.

Seconds later, a low rotor horn validated Bray's decision to begin responding to the emergency. Unable to continue powered flight to the nearby field, he entered an autorotation and headed for the only spot available to him, a two-lane road lined by trees and concrete light posts.

TFOs are given emergency procedure training on their first day at the Alachua County/Gainesville Joint Aviation Unit (JAU). That training also includes applying the information in flight with the same simulated emergency procedures for which pilots train. When the incident occurred on Dec. 8, DeCastro immediately recognized what was happening and applied his training, broadcasting the aircraft location and status so Bray could concentrate on flying the aircraft.

Bray's successful autorotation involved dodging not only trees and poles, but also a van that pulled out in front of him on short final. All too often, a successful emergency landing marks the end of the extent to which an agency has prepared for an incident. Fortunately, JAU had prepared an incident response plan and ran their parent agencies through practice scenarios.

The plan, available on the agency intranet, was immediately activated. For the crew at the hangar, the response was simple. One of them called the mechanic, and the other grabbed the incident response case. The case was always left out in an open area of the office, readily accessible. Once on-scene, the lead TFO took the case and sought out the unit commander. The unit commander had been in charge of the unit for only a few months and had no aviation experience. A hard copy of the safety plan was taken out of the case, and the two worked through it, starting on the first page.

The plan was broken up into sections, each dealing with different scenarios to which a unit might have to respond, from a missing aircraft to a known crash site. The unit commander was able to start at the section that was applicable to the incident and began working through the plan. The main consideration was making notifications. The plan included each of them listed in one section. The unit went through them one by one to ensure everything was done properly. Simultaneously, the response team used the plan and items in the response kit to document the incident site and response effort.

While the pilot and TFO were fortunate enough to escape injury in this case, the plan was designed to be carried out just as efficiently without the benefit of their assistance on site. The unit initiated a safety stand-down and grounded all other aircraft and flight crews, requesting a neighboring jurisdiction's aviation unit to cover for a minimum of 24 hours. Once the federal authorities confirmed it was okay to move the aircraft, it was quickly loaded up and brought back to the unit hangar.

It was a day that could have turned out differently. A strong safety program integrated in frequent pilot and TFO training allowed the flight crew to react quickly and appropriately to a series of challenges, each offering an opportunity for disaster.

The professionalism of JAU's actions continued with the swift application of a rehearsed incident response plan by other members of the unit and two responding agency members, many of whom had no aviation experience. Physical and emotional injury to the flight crew were minimized, and the incident was portrayed in a positive light, as the media and community were shown how a group of law enforcement aviation professionals managed to calmly stay in control.

The incident offered a real world analysis of JAU's response plan, revealing areas in need of improvement that had not previously been identified through training. The following lessons can be passed on to other agencies so they will be better prepared if the need ever arises:

> • The recovery section of the plan was incomplete. Better advance planning was needed on what resources would be needed to disassemble the aircraft and load it onto a trailer for transport. The unit was fortunate resources were quickly made available from the local utilities department, and the aircraft landed upright.

• While public information officers had been trained, agency press releases needed improvement. Several generic statements need to be written and included in the plan so the officer can pick the appropriate statement and read it.

• While the unit had an incident response kit with items needed to respond to and document the incident, a recovery kit or checklist so all items required onsite are available when the aircraft is ready to be moved also is needed.

• A section of the plan addressing securing pilot and aircraft records needed to be added.

• The morning fuel sample should be marked and kept until the next fuel sample is taken. (A fuel sample was taken at the scene with supplies in the kit. Neither fuel contamination nor starvation were considered possible causes of this incident.)

HUMAN HORSEPOWER:
How to Prepare for Unknown Threats

It is usually not advisable to wait until after a gunfight has started to load your weapon. No self-respecting law officer would even think of starting a shift without his or her sidearm being loaded—despite the fact that the vast majority of officers will never fire their weapon during their career. We know the probability of using the weapon is low, but the severity of not being prepared is at the top of the scale, making the risk worth the daily effort.

Law enforcement officers also know that when the time to perform has come, the time to prepare has passed. We must use the same approach to deal with the risks we face during our daily work in public safety aviation. The weapons we need to defend ourselves should be loaded up before the fight starts, not after.

Whether we are talking about manned or unmanned flight, maintenance or engineering, dispatch or air traffic control, humans will always be a part of aviation. The good thing is we will always have human ingenuity, imagination and unique decision-making capabilities. The bad thing is we will never be 100 percent error free. The only choice is to accept this fact and learn to exploit the benefits while minimizing errors. And the best way to minimize human error is to use methods maximizing the human performance available.

Just like an engine, humans have a limited amount of power. The tasking we put on a person varies throughout the day. And the performance available from a person varies from day to day, and sometimes minute to minute. If the power required by a task exceeds the power available, we are guaranteed a problem. Dedication, professionalism and grit will have no impact on the equation.

It is important to understand the limits of human performance, how to identify them, and how to predict what will be available during high task load scenarios.

We all know fatigue, stress, nutrition, physical health and environmental factors like heat and noise degrade human performance. What typically gets us in trouble is not a lack of knowledge of the factors but faulty perception of when they are impacting our performance. The indicators we use to determine when performance has been degraded to an unacceptable level are usually related to physical lapses, such as dropping something accidentally, letting a car drift onto the shoulder or the head actually nodding off. While these are clear signs human horsepower is at low levels, they occur long after our performance has declined.

Our decision-making skills are degraded long before physical lapses start to show. The most frequent culprit in human factors related incidents is poor decision making. If we wait until we see physical manifestations of compromised performance, we will spend a frightening amount of time unknowingly operating with a degraded decision-making capability. Usually, we get away with this because we are not faced with tasking requiring us to push our power throttle to the firewall. But we cannot predict when such tasks will occur.

Just like a gunfight, however, we can be prepared ahead of time if we accept there is a high enough probability the issue could pop up unexpectedly.

At numerous points in our career, we will come to work with less human performance available than usual. We know the same will happen to our coworkers. We also know it is likely we will not realize the degree to which our performance has been degraded, if at all. The fact that poor decision-making is a major factor in the majority of aviation accidents has been drilled into us since the first day of training. This includes maintenance staff and unmanned aircraft operators. So, prepare before the fight begins. Set policies for fatigue and crew/maintenance staff rest, and make sure it is practical for employees to stick to them. Perform flight risk assessments as a crew or maintenance team, and identify the issues beforehand so you can take steps to adjust tasking or staffing for the day.

Waiting until we are in the middle of a flight or 100-hour inspection is too late to effectively mitigate problems. That's like loading a gun after the bad guy has started shooting at us.

High levels of tasking do not enhance human performance.

Aircrew members know bad weather may try to kill us one day. Prepare for it before every flight. If the weather is not great but fly-able, brief your IIMC procedure and a preferred instrument approach. Load the instrument approach and frequencies before you lift off. Set enroute decision points to return to base or land ASAP when you have the time and mental facilities to make the best decisions possible.

Aircrew members know it is possible, however, unlikely, their engine may fail one day during a flight. Brief and train for what all crewmembers are going to do if that happens, before it happens. We know a pursuit or surveillance will one day lead to a difficult fuel decision. Set limits and alternates before you fly.

Crew resource management is not something that magically appears during an emergency because we went to a class once. CRM is created, fostered and turned into a powerful tool during all the little interactions we have as coworkers from the moment we walk in the door at the beginning of the shift. Kickstart your CRM with briefings, FRATs, training, etc., and it will be there for you when you need it most.

Some will say major issues do not happen often. They are right. The same people may say it is a waste of time to prepare, and we can just deal with the issues if they come up. But if we survive without preparation, it will only be because powers beyond our control did not lay task loading on us that exceeded what we could handle. In other words—luck.

A study by the International Helicopter Safety Team found the top three factors in the accidents they examined were pilot judgment and actions, safety management and ground duties. Ground duties, including mission or flight planning failures, preflight briefings and performance planning, were a leading factor in 37 percent of cases.

Every task we perform takes a certain amount of our limited human horsepower. All of us must expect that one day, with no warning, we will be given a set of circumstances that requires every bit of power and skill we can muster. The more decisions and preparation we make before the job starts, the more power will be available to deal with the challenges that come up.

We all have to deal with unknown threats. If we take the time to prepare, we can deal with them on our terms.

CHAPTER 2

RISKS
& MEASUREMENTS

Risk management is not an exact science. We continually try to describe safety with numbers, formulas and charts in an effort to make the process as predictable and quantifiable as the other aviation sciences. And in many ways, we have been successful in using these methods to improve the effectiveness of our risk management programs. However, there will always be elements of the process that refuse to be held to black and white definitions. The concept of "risk" is one of those free-spirited ideas that shift underneath our feet every time we start to feel comfortable.

When I started studying safety systems, one of the first lessons was to go over the definitions of concepts, such as "hazards" and "risks." I was soon confused, as the definitions seemed to vary depending on the book I was reading. Luckily, the definitions now used in the *APSA SMS Toolkit* are the same as those in the FAA Advisory Circular (AC 120-92A). They are good outlines that allow for easy interface with safety management systems:

• **Hazard:** Any existing or potential condition that can lead to injury, illness or death; damage to or loss of a system, equipment or property; or damage to the environment. A hazard is a condition that might cause (is a prerequisite to) an accident or incident.

• **Risk:** The composite of predicted severity (how bad) and likelihood (how probable) of the effect of a hazard in its worst credible (reasonable or believable) system state.

In a safety management system, we identify the hazards and then decide the risk associated with them. If the risk is unacceptably high, we formulate a mitigation to reduce the risk or cease the activity. Easy enough, right? Here's the tricky part: what is "unacceptably high?"

In the past, law enforcement and aviation professionals have explained away risks that went unmitigated as inherent dangers of the profession. You came to the job knowing there was going to be a certain chance you might not go home someday. It has long been a strong source of bonding and a badge of courage within the industry. I once heard a pilot respond to a safety question by saying, "If you can't handle it, there are plenty of parking meter-maid openings."

This attitude seemingly worked out fine, because when something bad happened, we just blamed the performance, decision-making or poor luck of the pilot and/or officer involved. Our risk mitigation response was to cast out or retrain the single responsible party, assuming they survived the incident. Any further thoughts on analyzing the problem were (and often still are) nullified by the inherent danger clause. This culture stifled our ability to create risk management programs. According to a 2005 study by risk management researcher Carol Archbold, only 0.04 percent of U.S. law enforcement agencies surveyed had formal risk management programs. Most of the agencies that do have risk management programs limit their scope to workman's compensation claims and liability issues, such as automobile accidents. They are usually reactive, as opposed to proactive, programs.

Society, for the most part, was okay with this arrangement for a long time. How many action movies can you think of that don't have dozens of officers killed and at least one exploding helicopter? Worse yet, the plot usually continues without any regard for the carnage. In our society, people think that's normal for our line of work, and like it or not, society defines what level of risk is acceptable. According to risk management experts Christopher Hood and David Jones, acceptable risk is a "culturally framed" concept, meaning society determines if a risk is acceptable or unacceptable based partially on our ability to control the risk. If we do not believe we can control the risk, it is acceptable. If we believe that the risk can be controlled (mitigated), it is unacceptable.

Fortunately, the belief that law enforcement officers have signed up for an inordinate amount of personal risk has begun to change over the past decade.

The societal definition of acceptable risk is the equivalent of the reasonable person rule and defines what is expected of us during any investigations following an incident. However, society's beliefs about what risks can be controlled and the value of potential outcomes is constantly changing. Take seatbelts. Nothing really changed in the control methods (seatbelt technology) or risk (which actually went down), yet going without a seatbelt went from acceptable to illegal in a single generation. A similar change in public safety risk management was underway when it received an irresistible push forward on Sept. 11, 2001.

What the world expects of us has changed considerably since 2001, and we are still struggling to catch up. Most books on the subject of public safety risk management, especially safety management systems, have been published since 2003. The International Helicopter Safety Team was established in 2005. The FAA's SMS office was formally established in 2006. The Airborne Public Safety Association's SMS Toolkit and respective training programs began in 2009. Throughout this time, industry safety professionals have been trying to take traditional safety programs and combine them with workplace safety systems, corporate management techniques, industrial quality control models and other disciplines to find a way to meet the new expectations set upon us by—you guessed it—ourselves.

AIR SUPPORT SAFETY

When the Space Shuttle Challenger exploded in 1986, there was talk of the safety culture at NASA, but it was almost an afterthought offered by the U.S. House Committee on Science and Technology. The original Rogers Commission focused on the engineering issues and decision-making errors directly involved with the handling of the O-ring operating range and launch conditions. In 2003 when Columbia was lost, it was a different response. The report by the Columbia Accident Review Board focused a considerable amount of time on safety management within the agency. The tone of the report is clearly illustrated in its conclusion: "They were convinced, without study, that nothing could be done about such an emergency. The intellectual curiosity and skepticism that a solid safety culture requires was almost entirely absent [which is] incompatible with an organization that deals with high-risk technology." We live in a time when not even manned spaceflight is allowed the excuse of inherent danger to write off hazards.

We have seen this same standard being applied to aviation and law enforcement. Here is an excerpt from an NTSB report of a fatal public safety IIMC/CFIT accident: "The program does not employ any policy guidance to aid the pilot in making risk managed decisions with respect to flight decision making." Another report cited the agency for "lack[ing] a requirement for a risk assessment" and recommended the agency develop programs for "pilot decision making, safety management and risk assessments." Those recommendations were issued to the entire chain of command up to the governor of the state.

What happened to just blaming the pilot and moving on? What about the expectation that this is just a dangerous business and, from time to time, bad things will happen? The standard has changed. Society has decided that more of those risks can be controlled, if not eliminated, and letting them go unmitigated is unacceptable. The best way to meet these expectations is to use a modern safety management system. There is legal weight to this expectation, and we are starting to see that in response to accidents in our profession.

This new emphasis on safety may initially seem like a nuisance. I am personally happy about it. I know there are new methods out there that can answer safety challenges previously left unaddressed because they were unavoidable costs of doing business. I think we should be raising the safety bar through the use of these new tools. The legal weight given to the expectations put on our safety efforts can be used to motivate administrators and financial planners that remain otherwise unconvinced.

The same variances that make safety science difficult to nail down also ensure that the profession is in a steady state of change. Those changes can be scary threats to our operations and liability, or they can be exciting opportunities to complete more missions with less loss of equipment and injury. The aircraft has already left the familiar base of what aviation safety was. It is not going back, and it's not going to wait for us to decide if we want to be part of the flight crew or sit back in coach and hope for the best. The choice is ours.

AVIATION UNIT LEADERSHIP:
Modern Techniques to Manage Risk

"Welcome to aviation!" It's a phrase that can be equally exciting and frightening for a new unit manager. Even if you have some background in another segment of the aviation industry or an extensive law enforcement career under your belt, you have a lot to learn when taking over a public safety aviation division. One aspect that remains constant is the fact that a unit commander's primary responsibility is to keep the people and equipment entrusted to them safe. Is your unit safe? How do you know?

Our first inclination when examining safety is to look at the number of accidents and incidents a unit has had recently. But this can be misleading, as the absence of accidents is a poor indicator of how well a unit is managing risk. The second indicator often erroneously utilized to determine safety is how long a unit or its operators have been in business. Just because someone has a lot of flight time or the agency has been operating aircraft for decades does not necessarily mean safety is being handled appropriately. Studies from NTSB, FAA and the International Helicopter Safety Team have shown the average pilot in an operational (non-training) flight accident is often experienced, with thousands of logged flight hours.

Your first step as a new law enforcement aviation manager is to learn what to really look for when assessing unit safety. Fortunately, there are great resources out there. APSA offers a unit manager's course each year at its annual conference. The Public Safety Aviation Accreditation Commission standards for our industry are available on the APSA website. If you are unfortunate enough to have an aircraft accident at your agency, these are the standards to which you will be held during the investigation. We know this because it has already happened. *The Aviators Model Code of Conduct*, which also includes a document for aviation maintenance technician best practices, is good to review as well: www.secureav.com/AMCC-v2.html. Finally, one of the best resources available to you is the APSA membership directory on the association website. With the APSA community, the answers to your questions are usually only a phone call away.

NTSB has released its recommendations for public safety aviation. They are a recommendation that, with minor differences, APSA has been making to its membership for years. It's important that unit managers familiarize themselves with these basic recommendations and determine if their agency has these important safety elements in place. If they do not, resources are readily available to make it happen, most of which can be obtained through APSA.

What can you do to keep your people safe? Appoint someone to be an aviation safety officer and send him or her to training. Just as our aircraft and equipment have changed over time to become more capable, so have our safety programs. Install a safety management system. Not sure if you have one? Is your safety program outlined in a binder separate from your operations manual? Is it a document that sits on a shelf or in a computer folder? Do you have no idea if current safety elements of your program are actually lowering risk? Are operations and safety seen as separate functions of your unit? If your answer to any of these is "yes," you do not have an SMS.

SMS provides a data based focus for your safety program that minimizes the wasteful guessing that often drives safety training, procedures and equipment purchases. It will tell you what is working and if risk is truly being reduced. When your boss or financial officer asks if the funding you received for safety had a positive return on investment, you can show them a definitive, quantified answer.

An SMS requires components that you likely already have in place. Putting everything together and making a functional SMS requires a bit of training. It is not an intuitive process and cannot be simply downloaded and put in a folder. It is more than a series of documents and policies. Usually, it will take one to three years to fully implement. Your success depends on a few critical elements. First, obtain the right resources, available from APSA and a number of other places, for safety officer training. Second, remember the SMS is your program; the safety officer simply manages it for you and the unit. If it is to work, you must support it consistently. Without your backing and avid endorsement, the SMS will fail to influence operations, and risk will be unaffected.

What can SMS data show you? In our industry it tells us that, of the millions of hazards to worry about, the biggest risks involve weather, training flights, and loss of aircraft control. The hazard that historically kills more public safety aviators than anything else is inadvertently flying into weather where the horizon is no longer visible, also known as inadvertent instrument meteorological conditions (IIMC). This is usually due to clouds, fog, heavy rain or darkness. This risk can be mitigated though training and equipment. You may find that your pilots and/or aircraft are already certified for instrument flight. Unfortunately, many of those who have died in IIMC were instrument-trained pilots flying instrument certified aircraft. IIMC training is a bit different than traditional instrument flight training. APSA has IIMC training recommendations available on its website.

Analysis of these high-risk categories shows that many of the factors involved in each can easily be controlled with a multi-person crew. For a second person to be an effective crewmember, they must be properly trained. In some cases, a second pilot is an option. In most units, however, a trained and proficient tactical flight officer is the best fit for both flight safety and mission efficiency. A review of the APSA accident database shows that for every one accident in a law enforcement aircraft with a second pilot or trained TFO, there are four similar accidents in single-pilot operations.

Another example of SMS at work is performance monitoring of fatigue risk controls. It is no secret fatigue is a big problem in law enforcement. When it comes to aviation, fatigue magnifies all the minor mistakes we make and often causes an accident. Fatigue accelerates vertigo and loss of aircraft control and impedes proper decision-making and multitasking skills. In aviation, there is little margin for error. The momentary dozing off that we can get away with in a patrol car is far more likely to kill an aircrew flying a mission.

Don't forget your maintenance staff members. If they make a mistake, the operator cannot simply pull over to the side of the road and call for assistance. More likely, your aircraft will be on the news that day.

Where SMS performance monitoring comes into play here is the overall effect of fatigue-related policies aimed at addressing the problem. Despite our assumptions of good performance, policies often do not work as intended. Minimum crew rest and maximum duty day limitations have been in place for many years, yet we still see fatigue come up in far too many accident reports. Why? They require employees to admit they are fatigued or have not slept as long as the policy requires. We leave the application of the rule up to the individual, and we all think we are far better at monitoring our own level of fatigue than we are. By the time we are tired, we are beyond the ability to make a safe and accurate determination of our current state. It is like asking an intoxicated person if they are too intoxicated to drive.

Here is the big question for aviation managers: What are you ready to do if someone does admit they are fatigued? Even your most dedicated employee will eventually have a bad night for a legitimate reason and come to work with less sleep than is required by your policy. What are you ready to do? Do you have someone you can call in to cover the shift? Is the agency okay with leaving the shift open? If you do not have a plan in place to deal with this scenario, it is unlikely your employees will admit they are too tired to fly and your fatigue policy will have little or no effect on your likelihood of an accident.

A final note on fatigue: naps. I know napping on duty in law enforcement is usually seen as a capital offense. But in the aviation industry, short naps are generally encouraged because of the extreme risk involved in flying fatigued.

What about the employee who doesn't follow the policy out of disregard instead of having a legitimate explanation? What do you do with someone after an accident or incident? "Just culture" is a concept that gives you a defined process for applying discipline that complements your simultaneous efforts to improve safety and efficiency. Studies have shown that over 80 percent of safety related "events" are due to system-wide issues as opposed to individual problems. In other words, what happens to one of your employees is a product of issues that are affecting everyone in your unit, not just the one person. Your goal should be to uncover those issues before they happen to someone else.

It is usually not the actual act in which the person was engaged, but an underlying factor. If someone has a landing accident, it is rarely because they forgot how to land safely; there was something else at play. Punishing the single person in question or making them perform the procedure over and over again with an instructor is not going to prevent the underlying factors. That response is likely to make matters worse, because it will keep others from reporting issues.

Just culture means you do not punish for honest mistakes that are a product of system-wide issues. This will promote reporting of hazards and incidents, which will allow you and your safety officer to find latent risk factors. And when the rare occasion occurs where the problem is truly an individual issue, a just culture adds backing to your decision to discipline or remove the person from your operation. An example of a just culture flow chart should be included in your policy manual, and the concept should be addressed in your safety statement, which should be the first item in the policy manual. There are examples of just culture charts in the *SMS Installation Guide*, available on the APSA website.

These are just a few concepts to get your unit started. When I recently interviewed a number of experienced public safety aviation managers, one comment came up again and again: "Don't try to manage aviation like you manage patrol (ground officers)." For better or worse, concepts such as risk management, just culture and fatigue are handled differently in traditional law enforcement. The development of these modern techniques in the aviation context did not come from a desire to receive special treatment. They were written in blood.

BUILD A STRONG FOUNDATION FOR SAFETY:
Tools to Manage Risk, Weather, Training, Planning & Performance

Safety is at the core of everything we do. In 2014, the National Transportation Safety Board released seven recommendations for law enforcement aviation. These recommendations have been addressed by APSA for some time and there were already resources in place to address each one, and many of you have been using them. There are more safety and training tools and resources available than at any time in our industry's history. The pieces to the puzzle are all on the table. It is up to us to put them together and push both our safety and mission capabilities even further.

Flight risk assessment has been a frequent topic at APSA's safety seminars, annual convention and safety newsletters. Currently, there is a sample flight risk assessment tool (FRAT) available on the APSA website, and a safety bulletin was developed in cooperation with the International Helicopter Safety Foundation on the recommended usage of FRATs in flight operations that can be found at www.ihsf.aero.

FRATs have become more and more common with law enforcement flight operations around the world. One reason for the increased popularity is people are developing and using FRATs that are more appropriate to our unique types of missions. Remember, the majority of a FRAT is composed of items we have always covered in our normal daily mission prep and briefing. The form is simply putting everything on paper to ensure we do not forget anything.

It also helps us maintain a realistic, analytical evaluation of risk when the pressures of a mission assault our decision making process. Make sure your FRAT is about risk mitigation, not liability.

If you had not noticed APSA's attention to the IIMC problem over the last few years, you probably were not a member. Since 2008, we have lost 16 law enforcement aviators worldwide to IIMC incidents. Those losses account for 59 percent of the fatalities we've suffered in that timeframe. A team of law enforcement experts came together to work on solutions. We recognized there were deficiencies in education on the topic and how we train for IIMC.

In 2013, APSA began offering IIMC presentations at its seminars and annual convention. A set of IIMC training recommendations were published on the website as well as in the form of an online course. Despite these efforts, in 2014, our industry still had one serious accident and possibly another with two fatalities (pending the accident investigation results) related to IIMC. Since 2015 we've had incidents, but no accidents.

We are constantly upgrading the technology and tactics used during our missions. Safety management is one of those areas that have seen some of the most dramatic advances over the last several years. APSA has been providing classes, tools, documents and guidance to members working on employing the most advanced safety techniques available.

One item many members have asked for is a "boilerplate" SMS that can be downloaded and put on the shelf after adding the unit's name. While many traditional safety programs could be copied and pasted in this manner, the very nature of an SMS makes this impossible. SMS is simply an industry standard that we all must strive to implement. We must do so not because it is expected of us but because it simply works. Done right, SMS will not only lower risk, but also increase operational effectiveness and availability and lower costs.

One of the core functions of APSA has always been providing the means for members to learn how to be more successful at completing missions. As much as I like to talk about safety, nothing beats a good tactics presentation or article. APSA has never been in short supply of TFO related information and training. And this is for good reason, because at the end of the day, everything else we do, from safety to maintenance to unit management, is intended to put the TFO's eyes on target so they can get the job done. Have your flight officers been to one of APSA's TFO or thermal imager courses? If not, you are truly missing out on a great opportunity to improve your operation's effectiveness and safety.

A well-trained TFO has two significant influences on safety. First, if the TFO is competent, there is less temptation for the pilot to divert attention from flying. Second, a TFO can assist in emergency procedures. TFOs can help avoid and respond to any unsafe flight situation you can imagine. I know firsthand how helpful a trained TFO can be in an emergency.

In reviewing recent law enforcement aviation accidents, I looked at human factors related incidents during routine law enforcement operations (excluding training, hoist, etc.). For every accident with a trained TFO aboard, there were four with either no TFO or an untrained "spotter." In 75% of the accidents without a TFO, there was an easily identifiable factor a trained TFO would have been able to help mitigate.

A separate analysis found a pilot/TFO combination could reduce the cost of conducting a search by 53 percent over a search of the same area by a single pilot. So why would we not use TFOs trained through a formal program? In addition to the many training courses and articles provided by APSA, I can provide a formal training program with performance criteria and standards to any APSA member upon request, which was developed in conjunction with several different agencies.

Dispatch and weather planning can be challenging for our member organizations. Most of us do not work for agencies that have enough personnel to dedicate a dispatcher to support our aviation operation. That being said, the type of service that a dedicated dispatcher can provide is extremely important. Just like in a patrol setting, the dispatcher not only provides that initial dispatch information, but also offers continuous updates on the call that officers use to maintain situational awareness. We need that kind of support in the cockpit.

The deficiencies in our planning process before we launch on a flight can be corrected with better weather reporting services, flight risk assessment tools and crew resource management. Most of our accidents are not happening at the beginning of the flight, however. The accidents more often than not happen later in the flight. Conditions affecting risk (of a flight or maintenance task), such as weather, fatigue, situational awareness, etc., change during the mission. An IHST study showed that the second leading activity being conducted when a helicopter crashed was repositioning or returning to base. It is this updated, in-flight information that we need to mitigate a serious threat to our safety.

Technology can help us to some degree with in-cockpit weather and dispatch information. There are new tools available to monitor and update flight risk information and applicable alerts for the crew during the flight. A simple iPad can now provide weather and dispatch information that we dreamed of having in the cockpit years ago.

Training for public safety dispatchers is another great mitigation tool, even if those personnel cannot be dedicated to support aviation 100 percent of the time. A dedicated dispatcher always knows where the aircraft is in case of an emergency. A quick review of public safety accidents shows that the response time to the crash site can be as long as a day when there is no set means of tracking and responding to an accident.

APSA has a sample emergency response plan (ERP) that includes a strong recommendation for some means of flight tracking, which is becoming more and more economical as technology improves. The goal of the ERP is to recognize the crew is in need of help, find them and get them that help within the "golden hour." Is your agency ready to do that? When was the last time you ran an exercise to see if you were?

Has your unit done everything it can to be the safest and most effective unit it can be? Before we can audit something, we need to define standards. We cannot measure the health of a system unless the measuring stick has first been established. This is not as easy as it may seem. Fortunately, the hard work has been done and these standards have already been established.

The Airborne Public Safety Accreditation Commission (APSAC) has published the standards for our profession. Those standards have been referenced by the NTSB as far back as 2010. Every year, more and more agencies apply for and achieve APSAC accreditation, which increases the professionalism and safety of our industry as a whole. I encourage all APSA members to download the standards and compare them to their own operation.

Even if you are not seeking accreditation, it is an extremely valuable analysis of your operation. Often, these standards are helpful ammunition when battling with management over needed changes, especially when those managers are not aviation savvy. It is up to you to take these pieces and put them in place.

INSTALLING SAFETY:
The Modern Means of Managing Risk

I am often asked, "Can you email me a safety management system?" The unfortunate answer is, "No." It is unfortunate because a modern SMS is simply the best way to manage risk without undue negative impact on operations or budgets. But it is difficult to understand an SMS without training. The nature of systems requires that each one is unique to every organization. An SMS is not just a handbook, binder or "cut and paste" chapter in the operations manual.

The good thing is that while much of the technology public safety aviation units seek comes with a hefty price tag, APSA members can acquire an

effective SMS on the safety page of the APSA website under "SMS Installation Kit." The section includes a guide and additional forms that you will
need to create your own SMS. The guide is broken down into six phases.

Phase 1: Set the Foundation. Setting the foundation of your SMS is
difficult but can be simplified by starting with a gap analysis that lists
every policy, document and process needed. *The SMS Installation Guide*
has several sample documents you can use to do the analysis. When you
go through it the first time, you will find items your program is missing.
However, you will also notice you already have many items, while
others may not apply to your operation.

Filling in as many of the gaps as possible is critical to the first step.
The *SMS Installation Guide* offers a number of resources to help you do this.

Part of the first phase of SMS installation includes establishing a
safety officer, or manager, and safety committee. The safety officer
should be an experienced agency member with extensive knowledge of
operational functions within the unit. If the safety officer has not had
recent training, he or she should be sent to a safety management or
SMS course.

The safety committee should include members representing all the
major job duties in the unit, such as maintenance technicians, pilots,
tactical flight officers and other flight personnel designations. The committee needs to have someone in charge of training and someone with
the authority to change policies and procedures.

Phase 2: Collect the Data. Think of an SMS as an engine. We have
built the engine in phase 1, now we need to start it. For an SMS, data is
like air to an engine. Without air coming in, the engine will not work.
This data is hazard information. What is out there that could hurt us or
damage our equipment?

Fortunately, we have already started to collect data in phase 1.
Remember those gaps in our analysis? The absence of many of these
essential elements poses a hazard to safe operations. If you have not
done it already, conduct a safety audit and equipment inventory of your
facility, aircraft, personal protective equipment, etc. Again, you will

find a number of items needing to be addressed. This is additional hazard data for your new SMS.

In phase 1, you will have created a hazard report for unit members to fill out. It will likely take some time to start getting these reports back from your people. In the meantime, conduct a safety survey. Limit the first survey to one page and ask the big questions, such as "What are your top three concerns?" or "What do you think will lead to the next incident?" The answers to your survey will create some of the most useful hazard information you will have.

Phase 3: Analyze the Data. Now that we have created the engine and started it up, we need to process what we have collected. The *SMS Installation Guide* has a sample spreadsheet that allows you to list all the hazards you have identified.

Before we jump into trying to fix everything, we must process the hazards. This helps direct recourses to where they will be most effective and limit ineffective, knee-jerk reactions. The "Hazard Report and Follow Up" document in the *Installation Guide* serves as a guide for both the initial report and the follow-up work the safety officer and committee should be doing. Reports require both a hazard analysis and risk assessment.

Hazard analysis is used to pull apart a reported problem or incident to see if there are multiple factors at play. Direct and latent aspects are usually present in any issue we are trying to resolve. The direct ones get an undue amount of attention. They are the last link in an accident chain, actual or potential, that leads to a harmful event. The latent factors are those that set up the opportunity or fail to prevent a direct factor from causing the unfavorable outcome. Latent factors often are easier to fix, and treating them can be just as effective as treating direct factors. The *SMS Installation Guide* discusses using a simple hazard analysis process entitled "The 5 Whys" that can be completed by either the safety officer or committee.

Risk analysis involves determining the actual risk of a hazard causing an accident or incident. Risk analysis involves determining the likelihood (or probability) of the hazard happening or impacting an operation and the severity of the outcome if it does happen. The *Installation Guide* has a document that allows the safety officer to set the definition of each level of severity and likelihood. This determination should be done in the safety committee. The risk score should be numerical so changes can be tracked over time. Usually, there will be red, yellow and green ranges. Once the ranges are set, every identified hazard should be given a risk score.

> "For an SMS, data is like air to an engine. Without air coming in, the engine will not work. The data is hazard information. What is out there that could hurt us or damage our equipment?"

Phase 4: Risk Mitigation Planning. At this point, you will have a list of identified hazards, including latent factors for complex issues, which can be listed as individual hazards, and their associated risk score. You will want to concentrate the majority of your time and resources on the red risk scores.

Here is where the safety committee shines. After taking the time to analyze the reported issues, the committee can move forward in an informed and effective manner towards controlling the identified risks. Efforts can be made to reduce the likelihood of something happening or the severity of an event, so the results can be tracked for performance. With all the diverse backgrounds in a well-organized committee, you will have the broad knowledge base needed to create truly successful risk controls.

For any major change in operations, equipment, personnel or procedures, take the time to run through a management of change process. This will avoid unexpected and often embarrassing side effects that even the best committee can miss during the planning phase. A sample management of change document is available in the *SMS Installation Guide*.

Each risk control will have to take into account current policies and procedures to determine compatibility. Changes must be implemented if they are incompatible.

Training must also address new risk controls, no matter how small they may seem. Simply telling people to follow a new rule or procedure is a recipe for failure. Again, the safety committee is key. Making policy changes or determining training is not a safety manager's job. If those positions are represented in the committee, the changes can be addressed from the planning phase through implementation.

Phase 5: Additional Elements. After you have collected information, analyzed it and developed risk controls, it will take some time before the results of the actions can be determined. You should set the initial follow up period at no more than 90 days because a high percentage of new ideas fail within the first three months.

During this time, work on additional elements missing in your gap analysis. Ensure you have an emergency response plan (ERP) and a flight risk assessment tool (FRAT). A sample ERP is available in the *SMS Installation Guide*. Your ERP should be published somewhere that is easily accessible for anyone needing to reference it in the field. An electronic version that can be pulled up on a laptop, tablet or phone is critical for rapid deployment. You should also set up at least one live drill to make sure the plan and the people involved work as advertised.

Even if you have already been using a FRAT, this is a good time to revisit it. Your FRAT should change at least once a year to reflect the hazards your organization is actively addressing. Over time, some of these hazards will change. You can also use the FRAT to see if your risk controls are working. Remember to collect data for later use in identifying hazards and checking program performance. A sample FRAT is available in the *SMS Installation Guide*.

Phase 6: Performance Tracking. If you have completed the previous phases as suggested, the final phase is rather easy. Unfortunately, this incredibly important aspect of an SMS is the one safety programs usually fail to complete.

This is the step that tells us what is working and what needs to be changed. It is also what helps us explain expenses to agency management and confirm performance to aviation unit members.

If we have targeted a reduction in incident likelihood or severity, over time we can see if the risk control has succeeded. If so, we can determine a new risk score. Since we use numbers to signify risk, we can track change in an objective, mathematical manner instead of simply declaring, "we are more safe." *The SMS Installation Guide* documents and spreadsheet offer guidance on scoring performance through changes in risk and determining future action.

Our industry has some of the most advanced technology in the public safety world. The tools we use are light years ahead of what most police officers and firefighters have at their disposal. Yet for every amazing piece of equipment we have, there are two more tools on our wish list. One thing that should not remain on the wish list is a modern means of managing the risk that keeps us from doing our job or threatens our return home at the end of the day.

IDENTIFY RISKS:
People, Aircraft, Environment & External Pressures

The preferred method of operational safety management has for decades been the risk management dartboard. We know numerous hazards threaten our safety, but we put them all on the same dartboard and target them randomly. As long as we throw a couple darts at the board once in a while, we feel like we have a healthy safety program. Usually, an incident has to happen for a hazard to earn a spot on the board.

Sometimes, we take information from outside sources to help aim our darts. While such information is important to any safety program, we need a framework that actively identifies our own safety needs, preferably before they cause a problem. And to create the framework, we must complete a risk profile for our operations.

A risk profile is a large-scale look at all the hazards in your operation. It is strategic risk management, not the daily risk management we often talk about, such as conducting flight risk assessments.

We simply cannot fix problems if we do not identify them first. Once we develop a profile, we can make effective and educated decisions about how to manage risk.

The first step is to determine which operations to evaluate for hazards. Most of us have a core operation, such as patrol or surveillance. Ground operations, anything from aircraft and equipment movement in a hangar to a UAS team driving to a location and setting up equipment, are an additional core component. In-house maintenance is another category to analyze. You may have several additional non-standard categories to add to the list of core operations—firefighting, SAR, prisoner transportation, training, SWAT deployment, etc.

Next, analyze the potential hazards in each group. List every hazard your team can brainstorm. Later, you will consider which ones carry higher risk than others. The risk profile development team should be composed of people engaged in performing each task evaluated. If you perform in-house training on any of the tasks, the trainers should also be on the team, as should aircraft maintenance technicians.

Try to keep your analysis "reasonable." You are not looking for crazy, one-in-a-million hazards like a meteor strike in flight. But you must consider the possibility things will happen that shouldn't.

Policies do not prevent accidents, but following policies can. This is why we need people actually involved in each operation on our assessment team—they know what is actually happening, as opposed to what we assume is happening. Remember, you are not trying to fix your problems yet. That will come after you develop your list.

If your team is unsure where to start, use the people, aircraft, environment and external (PAVE) model. Think of all the tasks given people involved in each operation. What are the failure points? Where could a person make a mistake, underperform or otherwise compromise safety? How could people get hurt during the operation?

> "Your risk profile will be a living document. Over time, you and your teams will find new hazards not previously included."

Beyond the trauma of a crash, what about hearing damage, thermal injuries, falls from ladders, long-term back and neck problems, etc.?

When considering aircraft, we must examine both mechanical and performance problems. What components could break during an operation? What aircraft parts are subjected to additional wear and tear during a mission? What are the likely loss of control profiles? Could your UAS have a component failure in GPS reception or flight control link?

In our environment, we must look at natural and man-made challenges. Temperature, humidity and noise should find their way onto your flight, ground and maintenance operations risk profile lists. Patrol and surveillance missions starting and ending at your home airport may not be threatened by wire strikes or terrain, but firefighting, SAR and SWAT deployment may be. For some agencies, the relevant environment is limited to a single airport, while others fly to numerous locations or land off-airport on a regular basis.

Finally, consider external pressures. Do sources of pressure impact decisions to fly or conduct missions? Are the pressures truly external, or do they come from unit members? When making go/no-go or safety related decisions, are your unit's rules clear about who has final authority? Is your safety culture supportive of professional decision-making, or are employees expected to do the work no matter the situation?

The next task is to give the items in each of your operational areas a risk score. Your unit should use a risk matrix, which develops scores based on the probability of a hazard leading to an event and the most likely severity of the event. Many risk matrices are readily available, including the one in APSA's *SMS Installation Guide*.

Once you complete your analysis, you will find some items are high-risk, while others are medium- or low-risk. The high-risk items should be given priority, followed by the medium-risk items. Low-risk items can be considered as time allows, as long as they do not interfere with higher priority items.

Starting with the high-risk items, your team should analyze the contributing factors and make plans to attack them where the error chain is weakest. While many methods of analyzing hazards and creating effective risk controls are available, I prefer the "5-Why's" model.

You may find some risks cannot be lowered any more than they have been. You can, therefore, accept the risk and continue conducting the operation or discontinue the operation. The aviation industry will always carry some risk. However, we should never accept it without going through a process to ensure we have done all we can to keep our people safe.

Your risk profile should be a living document. Over time, you and your team will find new hazards not previously included. Some will come in the form of safety and incident reports. Others will be seen in FRAT data, inspections and continuing education. Add the items to your risk profile, and put them through the risk and hazard assessment process. As time passes, your list will become increasingly accurate.

Review your list at least annually with your team. Individual risk mitigation strategies should be revisited every three months at a minimum to ensure progress. Your risk profile will also help drive your annual goals and objectives.

Understanding how risk profiles work for an organization, what can they do for us as individuals? Should we consider our personal risk profile? What hazards exist for each of us in the jobs we are assigned? What personal issues are impacting our safety in the hangar and air, and what can we do about it? I believe we can be more proactive than just trying to "be careful."

APSA's safety program offers an Organizational Risk Profile Tool, as well as a Personal Risk Profile Tool. Both can be found on the safety page of the APSA website.

It is 2020, and we have better tools and techniques to enhance safety than simply throwing random darts around and hoping for the best. Now is the time to know exactly what threatens your organization instead of assuming you know. And now is the time to press your attack, instead of waiting to defend against the inevitable.

ARM YOUR AGENCY:
Emergency Response Plans

I clearly remember the bright morning sun outside the office window as I walked towards it many years ago to answer the red "bat phone," a direct line to our dispatch center. "Are you guys still working on that county call?" the caller said. "We show you still out there." I was stunned by the question. We'd flown the call two days earlier. As I sat down in my desk chair, I slowly realized that if we had crashed, dispatch would only now be wondering where we might be.

I was relatively new to the industry and, up to that point, had assumed a public safety agency would be set up to deal with something like one of its own aircraft going down. I started calling other agencies that I knew had suffered aircraft accidents and looked into what NTSB reports I could find. I was horrified at what I found out. You should be too if you do not have an emergency response plan (ERP).

Fortunately, there is a sample ERP on the APSA website, along with a presentation on emergency response planning. The sample is a compilation of materials from numerous agencies and is currently in use by multiple APSA organizations. It has been utilized in actual incidents.

The goal of an ERP should be to minimize the negative effects of an incident. Chief among the considerations is to find the flight crew and get any injured persons to medical care within the "golden hour." With a little planning and practice, this goal is within reach.

Developing an ERP is a topic that could easily fill a whole day of instruction. Let's take some time to look at a few major points and common problems.

One of the biggest barriers to effective emergency response is the first step: initiating the plan. Too often, the plan is not put into action in time because the people we task with this step either don't know the aircrew is in an emergency situation, or they are not sure if the situation warrants using the plan. Clear criteria must be established so a dispatcher or supervisor understands when to initiate the ERP.

It must also be established that there is no harm in getting the plan started and finding out later it was not needed. It is better to dial back a response than to delay and play catch-up for the rest of the event. The initial steps are usually simple attempts to contact the crew. Several examples of initiation criteria are included in the sample ERP.

One of the critical steps in initiating a plan is in knowing the crew needs help. A state forestry airplane once went missing with no indication the pilot was in trouble. The crash site was not located for over a week. Most units have dispatch check on the aircrew over the radio. Unfortunately, this system is not entirely effective, as operators forget to check or we neglect to give position reports.

406MHz emergency locator transmitters (ELTs) have improved our chances of being located. However, caution must be exercised to avoid overreliance on ELTs. They are mechanical devices with limitations and have been known to fail. Even if they activate and manage to transmit a clear signal, the administrative steps in confirming the beacon, trying to contact the registered owner and assembling an SAR effort, is likely to exceed the golden hour. Many satellite-based aircraft tracking solutions are available, and the prices are not prohibitive for fleets of any size.

Often when writing procedures manuals, we try to cover every single circumstance imaginable. We end up with very detailed manuals that are so thick they become too cumbersome when needed. Separate the "what" and the "why" in your ERP by including checklists. Have a checklist with defined responsibilities for each person. These checklists should cover the "what" items, such as phone numbers, information to obtain, locations to check and other specific tasks. The checklist should be only a page or two.

Consider having separate sections depending on whether the location of the aircraft is known or if a search must be conducted. The checklists can have references to the rest of the ERP if someone has a question on "why" a task is performed or "how" to perform it. Minimize aviation lingo as much as possible (an extremely difficult undertaking for most of us).

Unfortunately, injured law enforcement officers are a favorite topic of the media. For most of us, only a handful of law enforcement pilots are working in our area, and only a portion of those are on duty at any one time. If one of our aircraft is involved in an incident, it will be on every news station in town and social media in a short time. The information will make it to victims' families at light speed. Your agency's ERP should include a section early on about how to get care to them. It should not be at the bottom of the list. It will take a planned effort to get to them before the media does. It is unlikely the standard family contact plan your agency has for non-aviation line of duty incidents will be sufficient. This, unfortunately, has been a hard lesson to learn in past accidents.

No matter how well you have written your plan, you must prac-tice it several times. What I originally thought was a masterpiece took four practice runs before we worked out the wrinkles. Your plan is dependent on the actions of numerous groups outside the aviation unit. If we do not give them the opportunity to practice the plan in ideal conditions, how can we expect them to perform adequately under extremely stressful conditions? Someone once told me their company felt that if a practice run of the ERP did not uncover something that needed to be improved, they didn't run the drill well enough. Take the opportunity to include as many

> "Arm your agency's non-aviation savvy leaders and information officers with the guidance they need to keep from writing one of those press releases that makes the rest of us cringe."

involved agencies as possible, such as fire departments, air traffic control, local search and rescue teams, etc.

Arm your agency's non-aviation savvy leaders and information officers with the guidance they need to keep from writing one of those press releases that makes the rest of us cringe. One poorly executed statement can make the entire operation lose credibility. One NTSB investigator said in an interview that improper press releases are the number one way organizations get removed from participation in the investigation. Remember, if NTSB takes over the accident investigation, it is theirs and you will only be allowed to be a party to the process if they allow it. Word your request to the NTSB carefully, as you will be permitted to be a party to the investigation only if you can provide technical expertise, not simply to gather information or "stay in the loop." And yes, the NTSB does have jurisdiction over "public use" accidents (Title 49, Ch. VIII § 830.5):

"Title 49, Ch. VIII § 831.13 (a) Release of information during the field investigation, particularly at the accident scene, shall be limited to factual developments, and shall be made only through the Board

Member present at the accident scene, the representative of the Board's Office of Public Affairs, or the investigator-in-charge."

NTSB and FAA will decide how much they want to be involved. When they are done, the aircraft will be released to your organization. Your insurance company will then do its investigation, if applicable. In the end, the aircraft will be put back in your hands. A big gap in many ERPs is the recovery plan. How are you going to get the aircraft out of the street, swamp, lake or building and back to the hangar? Have some options in place, including phone numbers and tools your maintenance staff may need to make it happen.

Many plans stop here, but several more steps should be considered. First: a safety stand-down. Take a breath and stand back after an incident. Go through a safety management-type process of understanding what happened and why. Do not resume operations until unit members are clear about the accident's causal factors and a plan is in place to address them. You may want to coordinate with neighboring agencies that have aviation assets and can cover for you while your unit goes through this process.

This "recovery" stage should include something that is very rarely addressed—mental health care. I have spoken to numerous flight crewmembers who have been involved in accidents. Most consistently regret they brushed aside the mental and emotional challenges they faced following the incident. I have known pilots who retired after surviving an accident because of unresolved mental injury. As most of you know, I have had the unfortunate experience of being involved in a training accident. While that accident did not result in anything more than bent metal, I have also been a first responder to an accident site with multiple fatalities. One of the people killed in that accident had become a good friend. In both cases, I was haunted by reoccurring nightmares.

These events had major effects on me that lingered for months. I never said a word because I didn't want to be removed from flight status. When anyone asked me if I was okay, I responded that I was fine because I didn't want anyone to think I was some kind of wimp or nutcase. In both cases, I was flying again within a couple days of the incident.

I am putting out this personal information in the hopes the issue will be taken seriously for others who may silently face similar challenges. We must treat aviation accidents the same as we treat officer-involved shootings and automatically give a few days administrative leave as a non-punitive, standard procedure. Require a visit to your agency's mental health provider before the officer comes back to work and again a few weeks later. Don't ask if he or she needs it, and don't send only those you determine may be having an issue. Picking and choosing will add negative stigma to those required to go, as they may fear being labeled weaker than others. If you ask, 99 percent of people in this business will say they don't need help, regardless of whether they actually need it.

When everything is done, make your ERP accessible to everyone who needs access. Put it on the agency intranet, on hard drives, in the trunks of cars. Then turn your attention to the rest of your safety management system, which will hopefully prevent the ERP from ever being used.

MANAGE FLIGHT RISKS BEFORE YOU ENCOUNTER THEM

What the FRAT is that? I have to admit, when I first saw a flight risk assessment tool (FRAT), I shook my head and thought, "There is no way in the world I'm doing that unless someone forces me to." But it turns out the FRAT can be a valuable tool in enhancing your unit's safety.

The name "flight risk assessment tool" can be misleading; this form should not to be confused with the risk assessment phase of the risk management process in your SMS, which is usually associated with a severity vs. likelihood chart and has more of a strategic scope than the FRAT.

The FRAT is designed to help flight crews assess the risks associated with a single mission. A number of variables are evaluated, typically including (but not limited to):

- Aircrew—Experience and training, health, rest, recent flight experience, etc.
- Weather—Present and forecast.
- Aircraft—Condition of flight systems, weight and balance, fuel, performance margins.
- Environment—Air traffic, landing areas, obstructions, air traffic control support.
- Mission—Type of operations, training and recent experience, safety equipment.
- Organizational—Recent changes in mission, personnel, equipment, procedures or policies.

The FRAT scores these variables and provides a total score reflecting the overall risk of the flight. If the score is "in the green," you are clear to fly. If you are in the yellow or red zones, you'll need to take action to mitigate some of the risks involved or abort the flight altogether.

Why add yet another form to the growing pile of paperwork required in our profession? There is no need to assess risk with paperwork just for the sake of doing something. (There are other professions preoccupied with liability that can do that for us.) So the question is whether or not there is a practical need for the FRAT.

Every month I think up a new article for publication. Usually, a number of individual elements related to a certain topic float into my mind. My imagination starts to tie them together and then paint them with explanations, examples, metaphors, etc. By the time I get to a keyboard, I am certain the article in my head will bring me a Pulitzer. But when the individual parts start coming together on the computer screen, they don't look nearly as good as the picture I had in my mind. The connections aren't quite as seamless, witty remarks don't sound as funny, and conclusions are never as clear on paper. That's when the real work starts. Sometimes, the piece is not salvageable and remains a draft forever stuck in my imagination.

The human brain tends to compartmentalize certain elements of an imagined task, such as writing an article or taking a flight. The connections between the elements are often assumed, which is why things sometimes don't go as planned. By separating the elements, their effect on the outcome can be diminished or exaggerated, because the actual effect on the outcome in real life is determined by the interaction with other pieces of the puzzle. Do I know the weather is marginal? Yes, but it is still legal to fly and I have been trained in IIMC. Am I tired? A little—I didn't sleep as well as usual—but I'm fine. The list, which we go through on a daily basis in our mind, can go on and on.

Each of the elements (hazards) on the list does not seem like too big of a deal by itself. Together, however, they could add up to a serious problem. Worse, in our business, risk is not determined through addition, but multiplication. One hazard may equal a risk level of 5. Combine that with another hazard that creates a risk level of 5, and the actual flight is a 25 on the risk scale, not 10.

The problem is with sensing versus perceiving information. Just because we are aware of a condition involved in our flight does not mean we accurately perceive its impact on the mission. In addition to the limitations created when information is compartmentalized, our brains may unconsciously delete that element if it competes with a desired outcome. As much as we would like to think the desired outcome is always flight safety, that is not realistic. We are in a mission driven profession, and the desire to complete a mission can easily overcome the desire to be safe. It can happen without us being aware of it. When the radio comes alive with the sounds of breathless, adrenaline filled voices yelling, "We need aviation, now!" we would be fools to believe our brain is not working against our flight safety decision making. Emotional corruption of the risk management process has killed too many of our brothers and sisters to ignore its influence.

This all seems reasonable, and the usefulness of a risk management tool that would give us a chance to overcome these challenges appears to be a good idea. So why is the idea of a FRAT so disagreeable? It is largely due to the same reason many aspects of SMS have been slow to catch on in public safety aviation: most of it was created for the airlines, large commercial operations and the military. The first FRAT I saw was a military form, and it was so long it had chapters. One study I found showed corporate and airline FRATs average 51 elements. About 20% of those needed review before taking the flight. I once downloaded a FRAT app for my phone. When I tried to enter the same airport for takeoff and landing, the program became confused (forget trying to enter an offsite landing). I had no ETA or routing for our patrol flight, which made the app completely useless.

The amount of time required to complete most FRATs does not work well for an operation that is responding on an alert status to hot calls. Even if the FRAT only took 30 seconds and the flight crewmembers had the time to spare, they would not be in the right frame of mind to do a reasonable risk analysis. They would likely rush through it and enter information that would allow them to fly. If the form identified heightened risk requiring mitigation, they would be further pressed for time to complete the most important function it offers.

Additionally, the information on most available FRATs does not apply to law enforcement missions. We often take off without any information on where exactly we are going, how long we will be there, or to where we might be called after that, leaving us without the data a commercial FRAT requires.

It's no wonder why we have not embraced the FRAT. But over the last two years, a number of agencies have begun using forms they developed in-house as part of their SMS. With a few changes to the traditional model, we can all begin to reap some serious safety benefits from this process.

For starters, instead of completing a FRAT for every flight, do one for the upcoming shift or "pre-load" one for any upcoming mission. This will give the crew time to go through the process without the pressure of getting to a call. Sure, things like weather can vary throughout the shift, but most items will remain the same. For the things that can change, leave the box blank until the flight comes up.

Another option would be to determine the maximum limit for the FRAT to maintain green status and then reevaluate should conditions exceed that limit before the flight. Say we fill out our FRAT and decide that if the ceiling and visibility drop below 1,000 feet and 3 miles, our score will go into the yellow. We can complete the FRAT for the shift and then monitor the weather as we normally do. If conditions fall below 1,000 feet and 3 miles, reevaluate.

The shift-focused FRAT can be used for normal operations, while a separate special mission FRAT can be set up for missions you do not normally fly. Examples might include SWAT/K9/diver deployment, firefighting, hoist operations, etc. A separate training FRAT should also be used to address the unique risks involved in the activity that causes more accidents in law enforcement aviation than anything else.

Does this mean we put everything into a FRAT and then cancel any flight that isn't ideal? Absolutely not. The FRAT, if done correctly, gives us a chance to look at the flight objectively and plan to manage some risks if necessary. If the risks cannot be mitigated to a reasonable level, it's time to stay in the hangar.

A NTSB investigator examining a fatal law enforcement accident once told me, "The first thing they need is a FRAT." I understand the reluctance to fill one out for every flight. I also agree with the disdain for many of the cumbersome documents that are out there. But by following a few simple rules, we can all implement this system and make our operations safer.

THE TECHNOLOGY OF TRACKING:
Know What You're Looking For and How to Achieve It

One of the many fun aspects of APSA's annual conference called APSCON is "window shopping." Walking through the hundreds of booths and exhibits in the convention hall gives us a rare opportunity to look at the various products on the market and talk to people that can answer questions about them.

When it comes to aircraft, camera systems, avionics and other products we are currently using, we typically know the right questions to ask. And for the purposes of getting info back to the boss, getting the specs for an upgrade proposal or just updating the old wish list, we usually know what to look for.

Unfortunately, this is not always the case for a safety management system. When the boss says he or she wants an SMS, what does it mean? Does your existing program qualify as an SMS? What whiz-bang features should one expect to find in an SMS? Following is a brief buyer's guide for the SMS customer.

It is rare to find a hazard that is not made up of multiple contributing elements. Your SMS should have a means of identifying direct and latent factors associated with hazards (or incidents). Often, we cannot do much about a hazard until we understand these elements and target them. Here's a hint: if your safety system responds to hazards and incidents by recommending everyone simply "be safe" or "just don't do that," the system is probably missing this component.

The SMS you're looking for should have a means of not only identifying and collecting hazard information, but it should be able to prioritize the hazards based on risk. Responding to every possible hazard ends up spreading your resources too thin and annoying everyone in the unit with endless warnings, no matter how remote the chances of the hazard actually causing damage. A method of prioritization allows the SMS to target those areas that will have the biggest impact on safety. It also makes sure limited resources are being used wisely and effectively.

If the first two elements above are strong, your SMS will have a means of targeting specific hazards. By understanding the elements that contribute to a hazard and the factors involved in determining risk, the SMS can target the weak points in the chain where you have a real means of attacking the problem. Again, you are looking for something more than "be safe" or "don't do that." Often, the risk controls will be aimed at lowering the potential outcome of the hazard or decreasing the likelihood of it happening. Each risk control should include a policy/procedural element and a training element, though it's okay for one or the other to be simple at times, depending on the control method.

A good SMS should have CRM built into it. The safety officer cannot be a lone safety ninja, single-handedly stamping out risk while everyone else goes about his or her business as usual. There should be a direct working relationship with the unit administrator so risks can be addressed with policy/procedure changes or funding when necessary. The safety officer also needs direct access to the training officer in order to address risks with training elements when required. These two functions are often accomplished through a safety committee. Without these functions, the SMS is a toothless tiger, able to identify targets but unable to attack them.

Finally, every member of the unit needs to have a voice in the program and access to program data and results. All of this should be laid out in the policy section of the SMS you are implementing. If they are not codified in the program, these elements will only be allowed to work when they are deemed convenient. Unfortunately, an SMS is often most needed when solutions to problems are inconvenient.

Performance tracking is a core element of an SMS. Without performance tracking, you simply do not have an SMS. Performance tracking means that each risk control you implement has a means of tracking its effectiveness over time. In the past, risk controls such as policy/procedure changes or training were written in stone, never to be questioned again. It was assumed they were effective. Unfortunately, sometimes our efforts do not have the effect we hope for, or over time they may no longer be needed. In those cases, we are doing nothing more than wasting time and resources and fattening the unit manual unnecessarily.

If your SMS has effective hazard analysis and risk control targeting, you will have an easy way to track the impact of the control. This tracking method should be quantifiable, meaning it should be associated with a number. The performance target should be based on measuring the effect of the control on risk. In other words, does it lower the likelihood or severity of the hazard creating the unfavorable outcome? Only then can your assessment of the risk control go beyond "I think we are safer" to "I know we are safer because over six months the number of accidents has decreased by 10%." A good SMS will also give suggestions on what to do if the performance numbers show the control isn't working.

Part of a quality SMS is the ability to estimate the return on investment (ROI) for any risk control. Again, if the other components of your

SMS work well, you will be targeting a specific hazard based on distinct risk parameters and with a defined, quantifiable goal. Another way of prioritizing which hazards should be targeted and tracking those you choose to address is to look at ROI. If a hazard causes an unfavorable outcome (accident, injury, loss of use, accelerated equipment wear, etc.) what will it cost you? Subtract from that the cost of implementation of the control. The difference between the two numbers gives you an estimate of ROI.

> "By understanding the elements that contribute to a hazard and the factors involved in determining risk, the SMS can target the weak points in the chain where you have a real means of attacking the problem."

You can further adjust the ROI using "probability of success," which estimates the likelihood the risk control will be implemented as planned and will have the desired effect. No plan is perfect, so this adjustment will decrease your ROI estimate. However, by doing this you will have a more accurate ROI that others will find more reasonable. This is important because outside of tracking the performance of the SMS, ROI is useful in selling the program and proposed risk controls to agency administrators. Your time and resources may only allow you to take the time to calculate ROI on big-ticket items. However, it is nice to track all of your efforts so you can show unit members and the bosses what they have been getting for their money. Such evidence is especially useful when the lack of actual accidents or incidents has created the illusion that safety efforts are not needed.

Whether or not you purchase an SMS or create one yourself, know what you are looking for. There are many other features and components to an SMS beyond those listed here. However, without these few essential components, you will not be getting the intended positive effect.

We all have long wish lists filled with equipment, training and air-craft. Over time, we have upgraded our programs with many items on those wish lists, often because we had the right answers when the boss asked us where to send the next chunk of funding. Most of us have not upgraded our safety systems and are still working with archaic programs.

It is time to collect the right answers to your SMS upgrade questions so we can have a modern means of sending everyone home at the end of every shift. An effective SMS is the most important item you can put on your wish list, because without it, everything else becomes a moot point. Even if an accident doesn't kill or injure you, many of our units are just one accident away from going out of business.

MARKETING & METRICS:
How Safety Measures Up

Public safety aviators often resist safety efforts because they have misconceptions about what is being implemented and why. Operations personnel do not like wasteful safety procedures and equipment holding them back from doing their job. Management is suspicious the "safety" label is added indiscriminately to new equipment and training requests to justify them. And just the words "risk management" make most pilots and public safety officers look for the nearest exit from the room.

Our safety managers need help from a good marketing campaign. The first step is admitting the safety label alone is not good enough to maximize buy-in from our people. In many cases, it has the exact opposite effect. We need everyone to understand why they need a safety program and the safety products we deliver.

Specifically, we must address two target groups for buy-in: 1) our aircrew members, aircraft maintainers and anyone else on the operations level, and 2) managers and anyone else on the administrative level.

Before we can market a product, we must ensure we

> "Start by taking out opinion and misconception. Use a quantified risk matrix. This is the first step in marketing safety. It shows you are dealing with real issues, which can be measured and tracked."

have a good product. Let's face it: many safety initiatives involve poorly thought-out operational Band-Aids, often meant only to protect organizations from liability the next time someone makes a mistake. One of the main purposes of a safety management system is to develop effective risk management solutions supporting operations instead of hampering them. The systems should help avoid knee-jerk responses to accidents and incidents. And if we use them correctly, we should have a great safety product to sell.

Instead of telling personnel you've instituted a new policy and it must be followed or else, explain how the change helps operations. Perhaps the proposal addresses an issue previously limiting aircraft availability or leading to flights being canceled. Explain the process behind the plan, and consider using the 5-Why's model, which helps develop realistic plans and explain them. If people feel a new policy or procedure comes from a reasonable process, they are likely to buy into it.

Involve new policy/procedure users in development. Aviators are not known to enjoy being told what to do, but we are known for being thoughtful and imaginative. For your safety program, tap into the ideas your personnel might have and involve them in safety efforts. It is easier to sell a product to someone who helped develop it.

For administrators, explain safety in terms they understand. We must combat the idea that our safety concerns are not real issues but disguised desires and unsupported opinions. Use a systematic process. How did you obtain your information? What is the risk based on reasonable estimates of probability or severity? How have your efforts lowered risk? How has the effort saved money or improved operations? Simple statements assuming we have improved because we spent money produce minimal buy-in.

Most of our administrators have no aviation background, and public safety organizations generally do a poor job of true risk management. The majority of public safety risk management work involves slip/trip/fall-type medical claims, lawsuits, and traffic accident claims. Rarely do we make an effort to identify root causes or develop systematic risk control procedures. Usually, we use the "blame and shame" corrective measure.

Start by taking out opinion and misconception. Use a quantified risk matrix. This is the first step in marketing safety. It shows you are dealing with real issues, which can be measured and tracked. Only then can we reduce the probability of incidents happening or reducing the severity if they do happen. We can track our improvement, as well. These results prove the worth of our safety programs to others.

Put yourselves in the shoes of those approving a safety program. You have been hired to manage an intensive care unit at a hospital but have no medical background at all. The charge nurse comes to you and says the nurses need portable printers to print out labels for patient charting. Sounds reasonable, until you find out implementation will cost $80,000. You learn the lack of printers has not lead to any deaths, and you kill the proposal.

Now, imagine the nurses must make labels on average 10 times a day to mark the XYZ test samples taken from patients at risk for ABC syndrome. Four times in the last six months, samples have been mixed up as the nurses take them from the patient rooms to the admin office, where they print labels. ABC syndrome leads to death in 30 percent of affected patients. The hospital pays on average $1 million for each ABC-related death it misdiagnoses. The hospital has made three of the payoffs in the last five years.

Based on the hospital's risk matrix, ABC misdiagnosis has a score of 25, deep in the red zone. The nurses believe printing labels immediately after taking samples will reduce misdiagnosis likelihood from a 5 on the matrix to a 1.

You have no idea what the XYZ test is and have only heard of ABC syndrome in passing. You have never taken a sample nor processed one. But the nurse's proposal makes sense, and the problem seems real enough to be addressed. The charge nurse also plans to keep track of labeling errors and ABC infections, and the legal department plans to track payouts due to ABC related deaths. After a year, the nurses will be able to demonstrate the printers' impact on incident rates and legal fees.

Aviation departments would be advised to market as well as your charge nurse.

Marketing is highly dependent on quality verification. People are suspicious of advertisements promising performance. We wait to know something works before we believe the hype. In commercial marketing, trustworthy spokespeople are used to convince the masses their products work, and new products are often given away for free or at reduced prices to establish quality.

For our safety programs, we have to work just as hard to prove effectiveness. We do so through safety program performance reports. Reports help us show our customers the issues we have identified and how our program reduces associated risks. They also show how the reduced risks allow for more flights, fewer maintenance problems, increased pilot proficiency, etc. The people reading the charge nurse's report may not know what ABC syndrome is, but they understand a reduced risk score.

I have seen successful safety programs help aviation units acquire new equipment like NVGs and flight simulators, additional personnel and new training opportunities. Make sure your people know the benefits of your safety program, and they will be more likely to participate.

What if your numbers show an initiative doesn't reduce risk? It will hurt your program, right? Not necessarily. People dislike safety initiatives when they waste time, effort or money. Your safety program is going to be under the suspicion it is somehow an administrative drain on resources. But you can prove your program's worth by showing you do not tolerate poor performance. If an initiative does not have the desired effect, change it. The effort will improve buy-in and support the idea that every product the program puts out meets a minimum quality standard.

Release reports at least twice a year. The reports should not be lengthy, because the average person will not read beyond the first or second page. Include what your program is currently addressing, why, and how. Show your performance on the issues and what you plan to do for the next six months. Send brief reports to your personnel more frequently, such as during quarterly safety committee meetings or with safety inspection results, but be careful not to send too much. As with any marketing effort, pictures, charts and diagrams will improve the effect exponentially.

Remember, you will rarely achieve 100 percent buy-in from your people. Someone will refuse to accept your safety program no matter how hard you try. Make your best effort, and focus on those willing to give the program a chance. Minimize the doubters' negative impact by sticking to the processes you have established and making the program as objective and scientific as possible. When the naysayers submit a complaint, process it promptly and with the same risk matrix you use for every hazard report.

Marketing is fundamental to any safety program's success. An SMS cannot function without the participation of the people involved in the organization it serves. Employees and managers will not participate in a program they do not believe in. Unfortunately, poorly implemented safety programs have run rampant for decades, dumping the burden of proving their worth in our laps. Telling your customers what you want to do is because of "safety" will not work. You must prove to them what you are doing works because of ABC and a little XY and Z.

COMMON LINKS:
Safety & Risk Assessments for Manned & Unmanned Public Safety Operations

Airborne public safety aviation covers a broad range of missions and equipment. We may be tasked with searching for criminals, finding missing persons, documenting scenes, providing surveillance, fighting fires, or rescuing injured persons, just to mention a few. To get the job done, we use fixed-wing and rotary-wing aircraft, both manned and un-manned. Despite the differences between the platforms, some fundamental and universal elements of our profession apply to us all. One is our association's slogan: "To Serve, Save and Protect from the Air."

Another common thread for all of our operation types is the need for a systematic safety management system. Whether you are flying manned or unmanned aircraft, following are a few basic steps you can take to ensure your program is efficient and safe.

1) Identify hazards. Some hazards will be obvious to you; others will be in your safety "blind spots," which are the ones you need to worry about most. Use a process that involves many sources to uncover as many as possible:

> a. Conduct a safety survey of all unit members. Different per-spectives on the operation allow for overlap that can bring light to blind spots. Make the survey simple and not more than one to two pages. Ask unit members about top hazards and what will most likely lead to an accident. Ask what they think should be done about the hazards. Other useful questions include ask-ing what safety element they think is working well and if they would feel comfortable reporting a safety concern or incident.

b. Have a reporting system so members can offer their input on hazards they feel need to be addressed. Create an anonymous reporting option.

c. Conduct an audit of your operation. A sample audit is available in the SMS Installation Kit on the APSA website. You can also use the Airborne Public Safety Accreditation Commission's standards available on the website to audit your program. The commission has standards for law enforcement, fire, search and rescue, light sport and UAS operations.

2) **Address common hazards.** Even unmanned operators must consider these hazards:

a. Human factors. People do not have to be in an aircraft to influence safety. Fatigue, stress, medication, operational pressure, task saturation and other human factors need to be identified and addressed. Human factors hazards can be mitigated through policies and flight risk assessment tools that control performance limitations related to fatigue, training recurrence, etc.

b. Quality maintenance. Maintenance is not something to be taken lightly, even for unmanned aircraft. Have a system for ensuring aircraft airworthiness. For unmanned aircraft, this includes software updates, battery conditioning, and aircraft component inspection and replacement schedules. Human factors should be considered in maintenance as well.

c. Mission specialist training. The importance of training for aircrew positions other than pilot is paramount to the success of the unit and operational safety. A significant number of tasks are required to complete any airborne public safety mission, but we can only do one task at a time. A trained and skilled tactical flight officer, crew chief, hoist operator or visual observer during a UAS mission not only increases the chances of meeting mission objectives, but also allows the pilot to concentrate on operating the aircraft instead of running the mission. Crew resource management is a critical safety management element that cannot take place if the TFO or visual observer are not trained crewmembers.

3) Process hazards to create effective risk controls. Often, we respond to a hazard by saying, "this is a hazard, so don't do it." These reactions rarely are effective. Here are a few steps all operators should take:

a. Assess risk. Your hazard list can become long. Trying to attack hazards all at once will overwhelm your safety system. Assessing risk is relatively quick and simple. Using a risk assessment chart, determine the probability the hazard will lead to an accident or incident and the severity of the most probable outcome. Use an assessment that assigns a number, not a letter, to each risk level. This will allow you to track changes over time.

b. Look for the links in the chain. Go beyond the operationally shallow final links in the chain on which we often concentrate. Consider the final error, omission or poor decision and ask, "why did that happen?" When you answer, again ask why or how the new condition happened. Keep going. Try to go at least five steps away from the final link. Each answer will give you an opportunity to control the hazard and prevent future problems. Deeper insights offer system wide fixes that tend to be more effective.

c. Process hazards as a group. A safety committee may seem like a big undertaking in operations with few staff members. It does not have to be. It could include everyone in the unit. The goal is to have multiple points of view and the broadest information base possible by including people with different training and experiences.

d. Assign tasks. Assign any new risk control to a specific person or group and assign a follow-up date. An initial follow-up date should be made no more than 90 days out, as most new efforts fail within the first three months. The risk control does not need to be in place by then, it just needs to be moving in the right direction.

e. Target risk. Your risk control should be aimed at reducing the risk of a hazard creating an unfavorable event or lowering the

Risk Assessment Chart		Probability				
		5	4	3	2	1
Severity		Frequent	Probable	Occasional	Remote	Improbable
5	Catastrophic	25	20	15	10	5
4	Critical	20	16	12	8	4
3	Marginal	15	12	9	6	3
2	Negligible	10	8	6	4	2
1	Reputation/Brand /Support	5	4	3	2	1

severity of the event if it does occur. Track the change in risk over time.

4) **Integrate promotion and education.** Telling everyone to "be safe" is nice, but it does little to promote the safe operation of aircraft. Instead of telling people to be vigilant, let them know what specific hazards have been identified in your operation. Provide educational materials and guidance specifically targeting the hazards and creating the highest risk at your unit. Let unit members know what to do to reduce the probability or severity of incidents.

5) **Track your results.** Do not assume things are working. Risk controls do not always work as planned. Policies and procedures sometimes become ineffective over time. If you made a quantified risk assessment in the beginning, check it again after a predetermined time period. Has the probability or severity changed? What is the new risk score? If the risk score is not acceptable, do not keep using the same risk control; change something. Be in love with the results, not the means.

Imagine we establish a new UAS operation in 2018 and decide to conduct a safety survey along with an internal audit based on the accreditation standards. In our survey, 90 percent of the unit members list mid-air collision with local news helicopters and fatigue as top concerns. Through our internal audit, we note the standards require a fire extinguisher to be readily available on site.

We have identified a number of hazards, but these two score high on our risk assessment chart. Based on the specific conditions at our operation, let's say the threat of a mid-air collision scores a 20 and fatigue 15. We recently had an issue with one of our lithium-ion batteries and realize the risk score for future incidents is a 15 as well.

Over the past six months, our UAS pilots have had to divert or land three times due to news helicopters arriving overhead at low altitude. Through a series of "why" questions, we realize we have never talked to the local news helicopter operators about sharing airspace. We also realize there is no method to tell the organizations our sUAS is operating above a scene. To reduce the probability associated with the hazard, we set up a training day and invite the local news operators. As part of the training, we also determine the best way to contact them and let them know when and where we will be operating.

Next, we ask why our members are concerned about fatigue. They say they are being called back to work nearly once a week within a few hours of finishing their 12-hour shift. We determine no guidance has been given to our communications center about who to call or when. They have simply been going through a unit roster randomly. We also determine a call-out schedule is needed to ensure the right people are being called at the right time. The efforts are aimed at reducing the probability of fatigue leading to an incident.

Finally, we target the hazard presented by battery fires. Through the standards, we see we should have a fire extinguisher available during operations. Purchasing a fire extinguisher does not lower the probability of a fire. Our risk control is directed at lowering the severity of an incident.

In addition to implementing call-out procedures, contacting ENG operators and purchasing a fire extinguisher, we can find educational materials to send to all unit members related to the topics.

After 90 days, we revisit our three risk controls. Let's say the meeting with the news operators went well and we now have a written memorandum of understanding with them laying out communications and aircraft separation procedures. It has only been 90 days but we have not had another incident. It seems like the probability of the risk has been reduced but we need to keep an eye on it for the reminder of the year.

We develop a call-out schedule and send it to the communication center. Unfortunately, we still had three unit members called after being awake for more than 18 hours. We need to go back and reevaluate the control to see what is not working. We have to be ready to scrap the plan and try something new.

What could go wrong with buying a fire extinguisher? Did we buy enough extinguishers? Did we buy the correct models to deal with a battery fire? Are unit members remembering to bring it? The answers will determine if we have lowered the likely severity associated with a battery fire risk.

Safety is not something we achieve out of good intentions; it is a product of performing a job as professionally as possible. Safety is what we achieve when we do our job right, and effective risk management is an essential element of professionalism. Systematic safety management does not need to be complicated—it just needs to be thought out. The type of aircraft we are flying does not change the need for such a system. If we take a few minutes to perform some of the steps suggested here, we can flush the risk gremlins out of the shadows and blind spots and deal with them from our desks with a cup of coffee in hand. If we do not, they will come find us during a mission, often at the most inopportune time, when we have a lower chance of winning the fight. Risk fights dirty. We need to fight smart.

LEAD & LAG DATA:
How to Measure & Improve Safety Programs

When I took on the role of safety officer at my aviation unit years ago, it was the first time the unit had an officer officially designated to the position. I was excited about the opportunity and wanted to do a good job, so I researched every possible safety topic, tip, tactic and training technique known to man. When I was done, I handed the boss a safety program that was thicker than the phone book. As you might imagine, it did not work well. It didn't matter if the content was correct, the sheer volume of information and scope of work needed to implement such a plan was not compatible with a unit comprised of three aircraft, four full-time employees and a bunch of part-timers. It also far exceeded the attention span the average chopper jockey had for risk management.

A couple years later, I found myself sitting next to a rookie unit pilot, the ink still wet on my new CFI ticket, wondering, "where do I start teaching this guy about the dangers facing him?" Sure, I'd learned some lessons on limiting the volume of material to present. But a million things can go wrong. Where does one start, and what information should we concentrate on?

If we try to relay every bit of safety information we can think of as it happens to come to us over the course of training, we end up sounding like a nagging mom dispatching every possible risk facing their teenager before he or she borrows the family car. The sheer volume and unsystematic nature of it all makes it impossible to retain everything, no matter how well intentioned the participants may be. What is remembered will also be difficult to access when needed because it will not have been filed away in an orderly fashion.

Another approach we use is to look at accident reports and collections of war stories for real-world risk analysis. We take all of the final probable cause factors and turn them into a lesson. While a good source of information, these causal factors are often reflective of a single, final link in a long chain of errors that needs to be looked at in its entirety. By analyzing the final act that directly bent the metal, we remove the incident from the context surrounding it and lose critical safety information.

In order to overcome the limitations of these two methods, a safety officer must use both to ensure proper focus and scope are maintained. The best way to make sure all of this is done in a manner that hits the mark without wasting precious time and effort is through a defined system. A safety management system can help get the job done.

Following the roadmap established by the APSA SMS Toolkit, we start by examining the information created by the event. This type of information goes by several names, but we'll use the term "lag." Lag information can be obtained through accident reports, mishap statistics, interviews and surveys. Often, the specific information we need is not collected by an outside source, so we need to collect the data on our own.

This data is helpful in directing risk management efforts, but it is incomplete. The information does not show the number of close calls or otherwise unreported occurrences in each category. This information can be supplemented with surveys, hazard reporting and safety committee meetings.

Armed with this information, we can begin to scale down from the millions of possible safety issues and focus our efforts on areas that will make the largest impact. We are also armed with data that keeps our efforts from being labeled as personal pet peeves, which can quickly sabotage the program. When collecting this data, be sure to address flight operations, maintenance, ground handling and servicing, training, management and operational control.

For example, in 2018, the national data shows that controlled flight into terrain resulting from IIMC claims the highest percentage of lives. Autorotation training is bending the most metal in helicop-

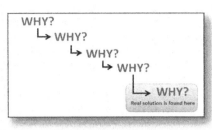

ters, while loss of control during landing is doing the same for fixed-wing operations. The majority of non-autorotation training accidents involve hydraulics failure training.

While this information helps steer efforts, if we stop here, we are left with only advice to be careful when doing autorotation and hydraulics failure training, avoid flying into IMC conditions unless rated, current and equipped, and try not to lose control when landing an airplane. Instead, we use these starting points to work backwards along the chain of errors. Many safety models and tools are out there, including the "Swiss cheese" model.

Another great method is the simple "Rule of 5-Why's". 1) "Why did Maverick run off the side of the runway on landing?" "He lost control during a crosswind landing." 2) "Why did he lose control?" "The crosswind component was within the aircraft limits and unit standard operating procedure limits, but he did not put in enough control input to stay on the runway." 3) "Why did he not put in enough control input?" "He had not flown in those conditions for several months and was rusty." 4) "Why had he not flown in unit SOP-approved crosswind conditions in several months?" "He set personal minimums that were below the conditions on the day of the accident and turned down flights if the crosswind exceeded those." 5) "Why did he take a flight in conditions that exceeded those personal limits on the day of the accident?" "The call was for a missing 2-year-old, and he felt compelled to go."

Through this simple breakdown of a relatively straightforward incident, we have uncovered important safety "lead" factors that set the circumstances for the incident. These factors cover critical components of a healthy safety program, specifically safety management and a safe culture.

With this improved understanding of the event, we can look at some possible interventions, or ways to keep similar incidents from reoccurring:
- Pilots cannot be swayed to take missions based solely on unit SOP weather limits when their personal limits are lower.
- Unit SOP must document pilot in command authority to cancel missions based on personal assessment of weather, even if within SOP limits.
- In weather conditions approaching SOP or personal limits, the pilot should not be told the nature of the call but asked if he or she can safely fly to the mission site and return.
- If the pilot has not flown in crosswind conditions within 5 knots of a personal minimum within the last two months, five more points should be added to the preflight risk assessment during operations in those conditions.
- All pilots should fly with the chief pilot at least quarterly in crosswind conditions within 5 knots of their personal limit to maintain proficiency and improve skills in winds up to SOP limits, where applicable.
- Determine whether a crosswind currency requirement or more crosswind landing training is necessary.

These interventions can also be turned into lead indicators that help monitor risk within the unit. The safety officer can track how often recommended training is completed successfully, if pilots are able to improve their skills and land in winds closer to SOP limits, how often pilots are required to add points to the preflight risk assessment tool due to lack of currency, etc. If these numbers are leaning towards the unsafe (e.g. low training pass rates, little increase in personal minimums over time, flights being cancelled more often due to high risk assessment scores), it is time to intervene. Intervention may be needed to either prevent another incident or avoid letting ineffective interventions bog down operations.

Over time, the safety officer will complete the cycle and balance the program by comparing the effects of the interventions driven by lead information with updated lag data. For example, if the number of crosswind incidents decreases, the interventions are valid. If the number of incidents stays level or increases, the interventions need to be changed so they can target different issues or be more effectively implemented as originally designed. This process of balancing lead and lag information validates the program, keeps the focus on target and maximizes efficiency.

CHANGE MANAGEMENT:
Using MOCs to Add Aircraft, Change Procedures

Certainty is not a luxury we have as aviators. We start our careers with uncertainty—about how we will pay for the training we need or if the market will need someone with our skills when we're ready. And the stability of aviation-related jobs often seems far too fragile.

Once hired, most of us live with a work calendar written in pencil, subject to rewriting so often it seems more of a suggestion than a schedule. Where we fly, what we'll do when we get there and what components we'll need to repair on the aircraft when we get back are all acts of a play with no discernable script. The variable and unpredictable weather we encounter is a perfect metaphor for the profession. Sometimes, we are tempted to throw our hands up and surrender ourselves to reacting to the punches thrown at us.

Change will come. Nothing can stop that. We can, however, manage how change will impact our operations. This is especially true when we initiate the change ourselves. Any time we purchase a new aircraft or equipment, explore adding new mission capabilities, or change staffing, policies or procedures, we must anticipate outcomes. Our world is full of examples of failure to plan for the full impact of new products and laws. We must not fall victim to the same mistakes and allow our organizations to be put at risk of injury, appear foolish or lose the confidence of those we serve.

The *APSA SMS Installation Guide*, available on the association website, contains a document required by the APSA Accreditation standards called a management of change (MOC) form. As with most things related to risk management, the MOC process is less complicated and cumbersome than many believe. The APSA document is a simple form outlining the main steps in a process that can save you time, money and the aggravation of unwelcome surprises. It also helps manage the inherent risks of major changes.

The first step is to recognize your organization must make a change needing management. Sometimes recognition is simple, such as when your organization is acquiring a new aircraft or adding a new mission like hoisting or firefighting. Any new equipment, such as avionics, survival equipment, ground handling vehicles, hoist/rescue gear and uniforms, should go through an MOC process before purchase.

Operational changes are the next consideration. If your organization is thinking of adding or changing any policy or procedure, you must consider the direct and indirect impacts and side effects. The power of habit is easily underestimated. If you have been doing something one way for a decade, simply proclaiming you will do it another way does not address muscle memory and ingrained routines. I have not flown a helicopter with an overhead battery switch in more than 10 years; however, I still find myself reaching up to turn on the battery from time to time.

Other operational changes may include new missions or bringing maintenance procedures in-house. Big changes introduce multiple failure points, which can injure both people and reputation.

Organizational changes are frequent in public safety. Supervisors change, maintenance personnel retire, aircrew rotate back to patrol and new unit members roll in fresh from the street. For better or worse, it is the world we live in, and it always brings challenges. But if we take the time to complete an MOC, we can limit negative impacts.

Not all change management involves permanent changes. Often, temporary changes cause the most problems, as we do not properly plan for them. Special events, natural or man-made disasters, and critical incidents are inevitable in our business. The MOC process for such events does not need to take long, it just needs to be taken seriously.

Even slight departures from normal operations can allow disaster to sneak in. Do you always launch aircraft from the same spot on the ramp or park in a certain area? What if construction requires using a different location for a week or month? While it seems like a simple change, I once saw an Agusta 109 sitting on a temporary helicopter parking spot at an airport undergoing ramp construction. The rotor system was wrapped in barbwire from a nearby fence. The wire was not well secured to the fence, and when the aircraft hovered too close to it, a section broke free and fell into the rotor, pulling about 50 more feet of wire with it. Would an MOC process have prevented the incident? Possibly. While no process is 100 percent effective, it is exactly the kind of problem a simple MOC form can help avoid.

After determining an actual or proposed change needs to be addressed, we must ask two questions. First, what is the reason for the change? Second, what is the desired result of the change? For example, if we are initiating a new mission, what is the likely scenario we are hoping to resolve? Or, what are the operational applications for the capabilities of our new aircraft, camera or mission equipment? The questions can be difficult to answer, but they set the framework for the rest of the process. If we cannot provide a clear answer, we should not continue with the change.

Next, we must identify potential hazards. What are the challenges that may arise from implementing the proposed change? The bigger the change, the longer the list. If you are unsure where to start, use the P.A.V.E. model (people, aircraft, environment and external pressures) for guidance. What complications could arise from the people involved?

What issues may arise with the aircraft, both mechanically and aerody-namically? What about the environment in which the change will func-tion? Could weather pose a problem? What about the airspace, aircraft ramp or hangar area? We can include impact on policies and procedures here, as well. Finally, what external pressures could interact with the change in a hazardous way?

The list of potential hazards is best compiled by a group of people directly involved in the implementation and operational aspects of the proposed change. Your safety committee should include the appropriate personnel. The goal is to uncover as many hazards as possible, espe-cially those that are not obvious. The more hazards you identify, the more blind spots will be erased. Don't worry if the list is long. Encour-age brainstorming at this point.

Once you have your list of hazards, you must determine which ones pose a significant enough threat to warrant action. A risk matrix can help your team determine the associated risk for each hazard. A risk matrix considers the probability of an incident happening alongside the incident's most likely severity. If something is likely to occur on a regular basis and cause serious damage or injury, it has a high-risk number. If the event rarely happens or is not likely to cause damage, it has a low-risk score.

Next, examine the hazards with high and medium risk and determine if your organization can lower either the likelihood of occurrence or out-come severity. Some hazards are easy to mitigate to a low risk score. Some will remain at a medium or high level even with risk controls.

Finally, ask whether the proposed change is worth it. Every risk con-trol requires money, effort or limitations on other aspects of your opera-tion. What is the risk to your personnel, agency or community if you do not implement the change? Is the proposed scenario rare and unlikely? Will the impact on the community be massive if the change is not imple-mented? By doing a risk assessment of the hazard you are trying to miti-gate with the proposed change, you can compare the cost of the change with the cost of making no change.

If you determine the new mission, equipment, policy, procedure or personnel is justified and the proposed risk controls are financially and operationally reasonable, your organization will be in a position to make the change. The change committee can determine what tasks need to be completed, who should complete them and when they should be done. The time invested in the MOC process is not as much as it may seem. And the time, money and pain it will save in the long run is exponentially higher.

Will the MOC process uncover 100 percent of the change's potential complications? There is no way to be certain. However, it is easier to deal with one unexpected problem than three. What we can guarantee is the MOC process will increase your probability of success.

IDENTIFY, MITIGATE AND PLAN FOR AIRBORNE USE OF FORCE MISSION RISKS

Can we do it? Should we do it? What are we trying to accomplish? Any time we are faced with a potential change to our operation, we should be asking these questions. Often, the answers are not simple. But we owe it to ourselves and the people we serve to use thoughtful and analytical methods to answer them.

The incorporation of airborne use of force (AUF) missions into an operation requires a management of change (MOC) process. Too often, we leave important decisions to knee-jerk conclusions. "Can we do it? You think so? Let's start tomorrow!" An MOC process can help us maximize our effectiveness and safety simultaneously by rooting out the unforeseen consequences that often lead to embarrassing news stories or even funerals.

Texting laws are a perfect example of a failure to plan. In the U.S., most states have responded to the problem of people texting while operating a vehicle by outlawing texting while driving. It seems reasonable. However, recent studies have shown that the texting related accident rate in many of those states actually increased after enacting these new laws. The problem was that people still texted, they just lowered the phone so they wouldn't get caught. This brings the driver's eyes lower and increases the risk of an accident.

Such texting laws were enacted with the best intentions. Unfortunately, good intentions do not guarantee positive results. Change management methods should be conducted whenever there is a change in your operation that affects the missions you perform, equipment, procedures and policies, personnel, etc. If you are making a change in how you conduct business, run through an MOC procedure just to be sure.

MOC does not have to be a complicated process. Like many safety management system concepts, MOC simply lays out the steps in front of us, removing the failures of memory, assumption and estimation that infect decisions made purely in our heads. The *APSA SMS Installation Guide*, available on the APSA website, has a sample MOC form.

The first step is to make sure any change is a group effort. This is a perfect time to enlist the safety committee, which may be everyone in the unit depending on the size of your operation. If the change being analyzed involves others, such as SWAT or search and rescue personnel, involve them as well.

Next, define the reason for the change. This seems painfully obvious, but it is often overlooked and cripples the rest of the process. The most important question is not "Can we do it?" but rather, "What are we trying to accomplish?" or "What is the desired result of the change?" If you are considering a new mission, what is the likely scenario? If it is new equipment, how will it satisfy an operational need or lower risk associated with a hazard? For new personnel, what role are they filling, and for what responsibilities or unit needs are they required?

In the case of deploying lethal force from an aircraft, defining the most likely scenarios your agency would be involved in will drive the rest of the program. Before deciding on the proposed change, look at the desired result and determine if there are alternative ways to accomplish the goal.

The next step is the fun part—brainstorming. What are the various challenges and risks involved in the change? What can go wrong? What equipment and training is the unit lacking? With AUF, we may find risks such as:

- Pilot being hit by gunfire and loss of aircraft control.
- Other aircrew/SWAT hit by gunfire.
- Aircrew/SWAT falling from aircraft.
- Aircraft damage from suspect gunfire.
- Accidental aircraft damage/injury from onboard shooter.
- Debris/casings damaging tail rotor.
- Hitting objects/people other than the intended target.
- Loss of aircraft control due to evasive maneuvering.
- Negative public response.
- Lack of funds/personnel available for proper training.

These issues must be addressed in the planning process. If you are having trouble imagining risks, use the PAVE model: Person(s), Aircraft, Environment and External pressures. You can also use a probability of success formula, an example of which is in the Hazard Tracking Log available in the *SMS Installation Guide*. The process asks a number of questions about your organization's prior experience, resources and planning process in relation to the proposed project. It will not only give you a reasonable estimation of the success of your program should you go ahead with it, but it will also identify challenges that need to be addressed to make it happen.

Part of your brainstorming process should be to use one of the most important aspects of your APSA membership—access to the vast knowledge and experiences of the industry. It is likely another APSA member has been involved in the same proposed change your agency is considering. Ask for input at APSA events, through the discussion forum on the association website or contacts in the membership directory, or call the main office.

As is the case with any good risk management process, we are not going to shut down the plan simply because risk exists. We must determine if the risk can be mitigated to an acceptable level by estimating the initial risk score and concentrating on unacceptably high scores.

Next step: mitigate. For higher risk items, the team should come up with at least one realistic means of lowering the risk. These mitigations (risk controls) can include training, equipment and mission profiles. The required investments in time, money and resources required to make the proposed change happen will start to become clear.

For proposals requiring significant funding, it's a good idea to calculate your return on investment (ROI). Remember that it is common to underestimate the time, funding and personnel hours needed to initiate and maintain an operational change. This is a major issue in AUF missions.

At this point, we have determined exactly what the change we want to consider implementing is and what results we hope it will have. We have, as a group, determined what hazards will be involved and the risk associated with each of them. The group has developed a reasonable plan to mitigate the higher risk items to the lowest level practical.

We can finally make an educated decision on whether or not we can implement the proposed change. With the information we've gathered, answer the following questions:

    1) What is the risk (to operations or the community) if the change is not implemented?

    2) What is the risk (to operations or the community) if the change is implemented?

    3) What is the estimated cost of the change (funds, time, personnel, etc.)?

    4) What are the training requirements (both initial and recurrent)?

5) What is the probability of success (0-100 percent)?

6) What is the frequency the change will be utilized?

Whoever is charged with making the final decision on the change can now make an educated, informed decision. There is also a clear outline of what will be required to make it happen. Assignments for purchasing, training, policy writing, etc. can be made, and a reasonable timeline can be set.

Anyone can throw a couple SWAT operators in the back of a helicopter and head to the firing range to see if they can put holes in targets. In all likelihood, if you get low and slow enough and fire enough rounds, you'll hit something. But before public safety aviators expose themselves to these high risks, we must ensure we are accomplishing something significant. Good intentions, skills and years of experience are insufficient by themselves to facilitate effective, reasonable and realistic change. A simple MOC process, however, can guide those same intentions and experience so we can keep up with and counter ever-changing threats to our communities and ourselves.

THE SAFETY CHALLENGE:
10 Ways to Reduce Risk & Increase Effectiveness

I never met Officer Shawn Smiley, but I think about him all the time. I went to his funeral after he was tragically killed in an aircraft accident while looking for a lost child. His funeral was both uplifting and heartbreaking. It has been years now, but I vividly remember the lump in my throat when I saw his three children saying goodbye to their father. I remember Smiley and his children to remind me why we stay committed to safety.

Safety isn't easy. Often, it is not fun. Frequently, it is not the most exciting topic of the day. Sometimes, it means we shouldn't do the "fun stuff."

Safety officers have a tough job. I find it much easier to teach things like mission tactics, special operations and emergency procedures. Those things are inherently exciting. We are predisposed with assumptions that anything safety related will be boring. The rewards of better tactics can be directly measured with more successful outcomes, like more arrests or thermal imager finds. Safety is difficult to measure and success is often, incorrectly, associated with accident rates, which may simply reflect good or bad fortune.

Safety officers usually have little or no authority. They are not supervisors and are sometimes stuck trying to gain voluntary compliance from people who think safety suggestions are an insult to their skill and experience. Safety officers struggle to gain support from managers who do not understand risk management or their role in it. And it is likely your safety officer is fighting this uphill battle with little or no formal training.

Still, safety minded people throughout our industry have been working diligently to develop a road to safer operations. I would like to challenge you all to follow that road. Here is a list of the top items that define the path. Consider it a safety challenge. I hope you'll complete it.

1: IIMC Training. After years of taking more lives than anything else in public safety aviation, the IIMC accident rate is trending in the right direction. The solution has several parts. First, the use of a flight risk assessment tool (FRAT) is recommended. The FRAT is simply a checklist ensuring the crew is aware of the expected flight conditions.

If conditions are marginal, crews are required to implement a risk control. One of those controls should be setting two en route decision points (EDP) composed of altitudes and airspeeds. These EDPs tell the crew when it is time to go home and when it is time to land. The weather minimums allowed for a crew to take off should not be at the limit of what is acceptably risky. The minimums should allow for deteriorating conditions and offer a cushion for the crew to get the aircraft safely on the ground before being pushed into an unacceptable situation.

There should be a policy that outlines what the crew must do if they lose visual reference to the horizon. The procedure should require declaring an emergency. This is true even for instrument certified helicopters and fixed-wing aircraft.

Planned IFR flight and IIMC are two different things. IIMC is always an emergency. The procedure should only allow for a turn to avoid terrain and obstacles. Otherwise, no turns should be made until after the aircraft is stabilized, communications have been made and a safe altitude has been reached. Unnecessary attitude changes must be eliminated, especially for the first few minutes of IIMC.

Finally, we must train for IIMC. Your IIMC training should not look exactly like your planned instrument flight training. Use a realistic IIMC scenario. Train the entire crew. Use simulators as often as possible. And include EDPs in your training.

2: Maintenance Safety. When talking about maintenance safety, we often discuss tool control, parts inventory and fall protection. These are excellent issues to address, and we should all work on them.

Often, however, we forget about the same human factors issues we spend so much time talking to aircrews about. Do we want our maintenance professionals working on aircraft when they are fatigued, distracted by a cell phone or without proper currency training? Of course not. Just as these issues are important for flight crews, they must apply to those we count on to make sure our aircraft are safely maintained.

Don't forget about maintenance staff when you write your fatigue policy. Have a policy to limit distractions when working on aircraft. Ensure maintenance professionals receive the same effort in training as other members of the organization.

3: Night Vision Goggles. NVGs work great over the city. They work great in fixed-wing aircraft. They offer countless tactical advantages, in both rural and urban settings. Missing person calls are particularly well suited to NVG operations. And I have made three precautionary landings over the years that could not have been completed in a timely and safe manner without NVGs.

But introducing NVGs to a unit brings new hazards that can only be addressed with professional training. On the job training is not safe or adequate. Get NVGs. Get them for the whole crew. But get some professional training. You will enjoy increased operational success, and you will be happy to have them in an emergency at night, no matter where you are.

4: Wire Awareness Training. "You will not see the wire." This should be the motto of your wire awareness training. Sometimes wires are visible, but looking for them is not the most effective method of wire avoidance. We must look for signs of wires, such as poles and support structures, straight cuts in trees or foliage, etc. We should expect that every road, house and construction site has wires.

Visual scanning for wires should be slow, with the eyes stopping for two to four seconds for each 10-degree piece of the pie scanned to allow for proper focus. The entire crew needs to be trained on what to look for and how to look for those signs.

Wire strike protection systems work. A number of public safety aviators are alive today because of them. If you have the means, have one installed.

Typically, an easy way to avoid wires is to put some altitude under you. Fly no lower than you have to. With modern camera systems, usually 1,000 feet AGL or higher will allow for an effective search while minimizing many risks, including wire strikes.

5: Fatigue Management. Self-monitoring fatigue does not work. If you are a manager and expect your crews or mechanics to come to you when they are too tired or ill to fly, you are setting yourself up for a major incident. Public safety aviation motivations are strong. Lives are at stake and budgets are always under scrutiny. Turning down tasks because of issues like fatigue or minor illness is rarely a consideration. Our own humanity adds to the problem. As we become more fatigued, our ability to recognize its effect on our performance decreases. We are left with compromised abilities and a dim warning light to let us know there is a problem.

We can protect ourselves with a fatigue policy and good crew resource management (CRM). CRM can be exercised during the use of a FRAT, which should be completed by the whole crew. I have been sent home twice in my career by a TFO, and he was right to do it both times. I was sick once and too tired the other time. I was too stubborn to admit the obvious fact that I should not be flying. Our CRM should always be so effective.

A fatigue policy should cover everyone in the unit, not just pilots. It should dictate a maximum duty day, maximum flight hours and minimum rest time between shifts.

The final element is the contingency plan. What will you do when someone is sick or outside the fatigue policy? Only three choices exist. One, have enough staffing to cover the shift with a second person. Two, leave the shift open until the assigned person can return to duty. Three, have a neighboring agency cover for you. Without at least one of these plans in place, we will usually not admit to being outside policy.

6: Safety Management Systems Installation. Done right, SMS work extremely well. But SMS are often poorly implemented, wasting time and resources. To do SMS right, send at least one person to a formal training course. Have initial and recurrent SMS training for everyone at your operation. Read *APSA's SMS Toolkit* and utilize the *SMS Installation Guide*.

If you are not your unit's safety officer, the SMS still depends on you. The most important things you can do are report hazards you see, participate in surveys, and give feedback on safety policies, procedures, training and equipment.

Use a FRAT, and when selecting one to use, ask two questions: How do I modify and customize it? How do I enter mitigations or risk controls for identified risks? If there is not an option to do both, keep shopping.

7: Professional Tactical Flight Officers. About three-quarters of accidents in public safety aviation (non-training flights) are single pilot or involve aircraft lacking a trained TFO. I have collected an extensive amount of TFO training materials that I can send to any APSA member who requests them.

A trained TFO is a significant risk control for wire strikes, IIMC, fatigue, loss of control accidents and a host of other hazards. Anyone who has flown with professional TFOs knows the success of an aviation unit hinges on their capabilities. There is no sense in setting up a huge stage and filling the stadium with a crowd if you are not going to bring a rockstar.

8: Aircrew-Based Emergency Training. Your TFO training should include all emergency procedures. The TFO or other aircrew can do something in every emergency or unsafe flight condition. Train for it. IIMC and wire strike avoidance are two items that must be addressed. Have a checklist for the TFO to use during an IIMC event.

Pilot incapacitation is a real risk. In 2016, numerous law enforcement aircraft were hit by gunfire. Bird strikes are a constant threat. In 2013, a police helicopter hit a bird that sent Plexiglas into the pilot's eye. The TFO happened to be a helicopter pilot, and he was able to take over the dual controls installed in the aircraft and land. Had he not been trained to fly or lacked controls, the outcome would likely have been catastrophic.

I have flown Bell, Airbus and MD helicopters my entire career with dual controls in the aircraft. I have never personally had a problem with it. There are no accidents or incidents in the APSA database attributed to control interference from dual controls. A word of warning, however. Training a TFO to fly and land an aircraft is work for a trained flight instructor only. Things can go from casual stick time to disaster quickly.

It is worth taking some time to evaluate how we conduct flight training as well. Almost half the helicopter accidents in the APSA database are training accidents. For many of us, the day we get our commercial pilot license, the nature of our training flights changes. Usually, we transition to evaluation flights. We fly with the chief pilot, unit instructor or factory pilots several times a year. They bring a checklist of maneuvers and call it a "check" flight of some sort.

The purpose of an evaluation flight is to demonstrate flight proficiency. However, a check flight is like our annual visit to the doctor for our flight medical. We do not admit to anything unless we have to, and when they ask if anything is wrong we say "no." At the end of a check flight when the instructor asks if we want to work on anything else, we look to make sure all the boxes are checked off and say "no."

Though we are always held to a standard when we fly, we need to have training flights that allow for training. Balance check flights, or examinations, with actual training.

Who is teaching the teachers? Your flight instructors should be offered recurrent flight instructor training. They should all agree that the day they think they do not have anything more to learn about flying will be the day they quit flying.

9: Continuing Education. "These are not the people I am worried about the most." I have heard versions of this phrase repeated by instructors time and time again at safety seminars and conventions. People who participate in regular training have less risk in their operation. The training effort itself highlights an overall commitment to professionalism that carries over to the cockpit or maintenance floor. The knowledge and awareness of risks gained during training fundamentally changes the nature of that risk in the operational world of each individual. It cannot help but be reduced.

Attend a conference or seminar. Go to a local aviation safety meeting. Check out the online presentations and resources on the APSA website. Go to www.IHST.org (www.ushst.org in the USA) or www.FAAsafety.gov and check out the free training resources there. The sources are almost limitless. Make a commitment to do something each month to better yourself professionally.

10: APSAC Gap Analysis. I saved this for last because it sums up all of the items we've discussed so far. I recommend every unit seek accreditation from the Airborne Public Safety Accreditation Commission (APSAC). However, even if you do not choose to seek accreditation, go to the commission's website and look at the written standards. Take them and do a gap analysis against your own operation. Anything that is missing probably needs to be addressed.

My own agency has gone through the accreditation process now, and I did not find any of the standards to be unreasonable. It may not always be easy to meet each standard, but that does not mean the standard is unnecessary. There is no doubt that if we all took steps to meet these industry standards, we would have far fewer accidents.

As I write this, the 10-year anniversary of another accident looms, and my mind wanders to a great man I was blessed to work with for too short of a time. His nickname was "Bear" and I was there when he was lost in a public safety aircraft accident along with "Snapper" and "Magic". Bear's son and my son share the same name. It is a constant, welcome reminder of a silent promise that I made to Bear's child and to Shawn Smiley's three children -- a promise that the sacrifice that their fathers made will not be in vain.

We have nothing to lose but everything to gain by trying to better ourselves. If we try to complete the challenge I have outlined here, we are guaranteed to reduce risk and increase effectiveness. We owe it to those who have gone before us and those they left behind. We owe it to the officers who count on us to protect them from above and the people in our communities who depend on us to keep them safe. I ask you to join your safety officers, APSA and myself, and together we can accomplish everything outlined here.

CHAPTER 3

TRAINING & TACTICS

MISSION POSSIBLE:
Safely Reduce Training Risks

"What is that flashing for?" I asked my instructor. There was no need for me to point out what I was referring to, as the yellow master caution light was hard to ignore. Besides, my hands were preoccupied from the left seat in the middle of what was supposed to be a power recovery autorotation during my unit's semi-annual CFI refresher training. Before my instructor could respond, the aircraft answered by illuminating several more caution lights, including the seemingly enormous red engine out light. We were passing through 300 feet AGL.

The instructor made sure I knew what was going on. "I think your engine quit," he said. "Better get this one right." There wasn't the slightest hint of worry in his voice. All I could do was let out a laugh, though there might have been a touch of worry in my voice. We were passing through 200 feet.

Any good safety management system (SMS) includes a direct and active relationship between safety and training. Without the ability to address safety issues with real training solutions, the safety program is a toothless tiger.

APSA Training Program Manager Don Roby has been active in making sure the training programs he develops are directed at the most significant issues identified. In 2013, we spent quite a bit of effort addressing the threat posed by IIMC, which has consistently been the leading cause of fatalities in our industry (16 from 2008 to 2013).

In 2014, we put the same amount of effort into addressing the training accident rate. Training was leading to more damaged aircraft in law enforcement than anything else we do. Not all training accidents are reported, and for each one that does occur, many, many more close calls fail to produce any data to track. Even with those limitations, I was able to identify at least 20 training accidents in the law enforcement industry during the last five years leading up to 2014. Each accident resulted in not only damaged equipment and occasional injury, including two fatalities, but also a reduction in services, severe budget ramifications and sometimes unit closure. The reasons for our planned focus on this issue were clear.

One of the most important things we can do to reduce risk in training is to ensure we do the proper prep work before a lesson even starts.

Whenever I get the chance to train in a new aircraft, one of the first things I do is pull accident reports based on the aircraft make and model from sources such as NTSB, the Australian Transport Safety Board, TSB Canada, and the APSA accident database.

Another important part of training preparation is to sit down and plan out what maneuvers will be conducted. This planning should include the parameters (airspeed, altitude, environment, etc.) for maneuver initiation, instructor intervention and maneuver termination.

It also gives the instructor a chance to analyze what can go wrong and develop a plan to identify and guard against any of the possibilities. For example, anyone training in helicopters with hydraulically boosted controls should be alert to the recent accident data showing the high rate of accidents during simulated hydraulics failures. Hydraulics failure training has the second highest training accident rate in law enforcement, following autorotations.

The nature of hydraulics failure limits the instructor's ability to correct for control deviations made by the student. This means an instructor must have tighter tolerances over the student than he or she would if full control authority was available to return the aircraft to neutral. For example, how many degrees of yaw deviation does the instructor allow in other maneuvers before intervening? For this task, the instructor might decide to reduce that tolerance by half before taking over. Whatever the decision, the instructor should plan it out, write it down and stick to it. The International Helicopter Safety Team (IHST) has a great fact sheet on the topic called Maneuver Initiation Envelope (available at www.ihst.org under the "safety tools-training" section).

Training can sometimes be repetitive, and most instructors like to throw in the occasional "fun" maneuver or an alternative version of a task to break things up. These maneuvers need to come from a list of tasks that have been put through the planning process outlined above. Unplanned and/or modified training maneuvers done on the spur of the moment have led to numerous training incidents.

During my private pilot training in a Robinson R22, I asked the instructor a question about the low rotor RPM horn. We were in cruise flight over unpopulated forest somewhere near the middle of nowhere. He proceeded to turn off the governor, roll the throttle down a bit and lift on the collective until the rotor RPM decayed far enough into the yellow to make the horn come on. He had not gone over what my response should be, he never officially took the controls from me, and we surely had not gone over what I should refrain from doing during the maneuver. It was nothing more than a "watch this" moment. Neither of us had any clue we were only one small incorrect move away from a fatal accident.

Tabletop planning should be carried over to briefing. The briefing is another critical aspect of safe flight training we often take for granted. This is where both the instructor and instructee get on the same page, reducing the chances of unwelcome surprises. If the student knows what the instructor's limits are going to be before intervening in a maneuver or terminating it, each person will have a better idea of what is expected. Of course, we cannot tell the other person what our limits are unless we have first set them up. This includes all maneuvers, not just the big-ticket items like engine failures. To simplify the planning process, you may have a general set of limitations that applies to numerous tasks.

Finally, establish if the flight will be for training or evaluation. If the goal is training, designating it as such will make the student more open to asking questions, confessing they are rusty with a particular maneuver or admitting they do not understand some aspect of what the instructor is asking them to do. If the flight is for evaluation, review the perform-ance standards for each task to be completed. These two types of flights are completely different in nature, despite often involving the same set of maneuvers.

When it comes time to head to the aircraft for the actual flight, instructors need to consider what tasks they will tackle first. There is no reason to rush immediately into the maneuvers with the highest risk. Start out with a few tasks that give you a chance to feel out how the pilot is flying that day, how the aircraft feels and the actual weather conditions (always as reported, right?). Making this initial calibration is especially important when it's your first time flying with either the aircraft or pilot. After that, consider using versions of the emergency procedures with a little more "safety padding" built in, such as more altitude, airspeed, etc.

This practice has saved my bacon at least twice. Once, while giving instruction in a Hiller that had just come out of its annual inspection, I decided to wait on doing traffic pattern work and emergency proce-dures and instead opted to let the student do some hover practice to start off. The student was anxious to get ready for a check ride, so he was a little annoyed at doing basic flight maneuvers but didn't say anything. After five minutes of hovering, the helicopter coughed twice and the engine quit. We settled to the ground and got out to find fuel pouring out of the carburetor onto the deck of the aircraft. Starting off with the easy stuff also gives the instructor a chance to get his or her mojo flowing. Let's face it, many of us in law enforcement are not instructing on a full-time basis. We may find ourselves going far too long between training sorties, and the "other seat" can feel odd for a few minutes. Be honest with yourself and your currency level.

A couple years later, I was giving initial NVG instruction to a pilot I had met that day. The student was an experienced commercial pilot flying an aircraft with which we were both familiar. The training contract with the agency specifically called for touchdown autorotations. The thought crossed my mind, however, that we might not want to start off with touchdown autos right away. On our first autorotation, I had the pilot go a little higher than usual and instructed him to do a power recovery describing the specific entry profile, when to roll the throttle back on, etc. The combination of atmospheric conditions, our weight, zero wind and an inexperienced NVG pilot helped to establish the glide profile of a dump truck. The extra height bought me enough time to roll on the throttle early and squeeze out a little more airspeed so we could recover while still above ground. Had we started from the usual altitude with the intent of terminating with a touchdown, the maneuver would not have ended so well.

None of our planning prior to a training flight will be of any use if we do not stick to it during the actual flight. Sometimes, there is an element of pride, or possibly denial, which prevents us from admitting it is time to terminate a task and go around for another try. Some instructors feel the mark of experience is the ability to "save" any maneuver and complete the task every time no matter how poorly it is initiated by the student. I would argue an ideal instructor maintains complete control of the situation at all times. Such an instructor always has an "out" to maintain control when a maneuver threatens to break free of his or her limitations.

Anything flown outside of the parameters set up for the training task will fail to meet the educational goals for the lesson and may be counterproductive. As mentioned, training parameters should have a set of criteria for initiating the task and a secondary checkpoint sometime during the maneuver that gives the instructor a chance to terminate the task while it is still safe to do so. Usually, we think about this secondary checkpoint when discussing engine failure training. For example: At 400 feet, we need to have at least X airspeed and less than Y descent rate. However, we should set up such a checkpoint for every maneuver we conduct because the "easy" ones can also result in an accident.

I was involved in a training accident, and during the flight, we experienced loss of tail rotor effectiveness during a simulated tail rotor failure from a hover. While there was extensive damage to the aircraft, fortunately there was no loss of life or injury, other than my permanently scarred pride. I share this story in the hope that it can help others avoid a similar accident, or worse. We were performing a relatively "easy" maneuver, and the pilot I was flying with had a considerable amount of experience in the aircraft and the industry. The weather was beautiful and winds were calm. The aircraft flew perfectly, and the pilot had performed my "warm up" maneuvers with no problems at all. My guard subliminally diminished.

As we conducted the simulated tail rotor failure, I noticed it was not going well, but things had not progressed to the point where I was scared, so I let the student continue while I thought of what instructions I would give after he finished and we tried it again. Suddenly, we were spinning at what seemed to be the same RPM as the main rotor and I was being thrown sideways against the straps. Closing the throttle stopped the rotation, but rotor RPM was too low to arrest the descent rate and we touched down hard, collapsing the skids on one side and allowing the main rotor to stop itself on the concrete taxiway. Among the numerous things I did wrong, I failed to establish performance criteria that would have triggered an intervention.

Even though I knew the maneuver was not going well, I did not think of stopping it until it was too late. As instructors, we need to give ourselves an opportunity to make the safe decision while it is still early enough to do so, not when we have no choice but to try and arrest a disaster in progress.

My instructor and I were still descending, passing through 75 feet, when his hands slid down to guard the controls. I knew I still had the aircraft because he'd briefed me on exactly what he would say if he was going to take them from me, and he hadn't said anything. I brought the nose slowly up to flare—a touch of initial collective to arrest the descent—level and pull. The helicopter slid to a stop with no further misbehavior. There was no damage or injury because the instructor had followed some of the first tips I learned as a new flight instructor: never conduct engine failure practice unless you are over a suitable landing area, and always be prepared for the engine to quit when doing autorotation training.

Training parameters defining acceptable ranges in airspeed, altitude, wind, aircraft profile, etc. are one important part of the complex task of risk management during training. Instructors need to have a hefty bag of tricks at their disposal to identify impending doom and guard against it. Every good instructor should be searching for that next technique they can add to their arsenal, no matter how long they've been instructing.

THE REALITY OF THE MISSION:
Industry Leaders Share Insights on Training Safely & Systematically

Aviation safety professionals often find it difficult to determine exactly why problems occur. Rarely is the answer a simple, single bull's-eye on which we can set our sights. Fortunately, many of the folks directly involved in training aviators such as ourselves are together each summer at APSA's annual conference and exposition. These are individuals with the right combination of technical background and professional dedication necessary to address our most difficult safety problems.

I decided to take the opportunity to ask several questions of the top experts in the field of aviation safety: 1) One of the common recommended risk interventions is more "advanced" training maneuvers. What should that training involve? 2) Inadvertent instrument meteorological conditions (IIMC)/controlled flight into terrain (CFIT) accidents continue to produce a high number of fatal accidents in the aviation industry. How can we lower those numbers?

Pierre Bayard DuPont from Enstrom Helicopters suggested too much of the emphasis in autorotation training is placed on the touchdown. He felt more work should be done to ensure pilots can safely enter an autorotation, including quick and proper identification of the problem. He also suggested aircrews should train for the missions they perform, for example entering an autorotation during a search and rescue operation.

The concept of adjusting training to meet an operational profile was reinforced by numerous conference attendees. Trey Wade and Kelly

Westbrook from Bell Helicopter said an important part of their in-house training program is to customize the program for the customer's missions, instead of using a one-size-fits-all method.

Randy Rowles, owner of Helicopter Institute, Inc., has a long history of working with major manufacturers to develop scenario-driven training and agreed with the importance of making sure training fits pilots' needs. However, he offered several warnings. First, the key to conducting training maneuvers like an autorotation safely is ensuring aspects of the maneuver remain stable and predictable. When we add new features to maneuvers in an attempt to make them "advanced," we add variables without considering the desired outcome. Rowles cited the requirement for an "enhanced autorotation" in the Robinson SFAR 73. Before engaging in such training, ask yourself what you are trying to accomplish. Without addressing this question, we are unable to control the additional risks involved in the maneuver and set ourselves up for causing more harm than good.

Kirby Ortega of Cessna said the success of his company's training programs hinges on purposeful flight training. Training shouldn't be done just for the sake of checking off a box or trying to fulfill an arbitrary goal. He said the means of reaching training goals must be laid out and structured by an operations manual and safety culture. Ortega said this has helped Cessna conduct training in everything from the 162 Skycatcher to the Citation 10, "without a single NTSB-defined accident or incident."

Jack Reichert of Airbus said he tries to maintain the same training philosophy he used to keep his pilots sharp during his career with the Texas Department of Public Safety. He highlighted the difficulties in balancing the need for advanced training and controlling increased risk. Maneuvers should not be made more complex to satisfy an administrative need; they must be mission based. "We have to train the way we fly—train to the mission," Reichert said.

According to Reichert, three things keep us from training to the mission: funding, comfort and increased risk. He recommended combating the funding issue by involving your boss in your work. He suggested many aviation unit administrators are non-flying executives who have a comparatively dry workday of paperwork, phone calls and meetings. Their lack of flying experience does not help them understand the value of training. By involving them in your work, they will feel involved in something important (and have an interesting story to tell in staff meetings).

Comfort can work against us through what I have referred to as the "brother-in-law" checkride, which occurs when the pilot and instructor are familiar enough with each other to lower performance standards. Our training must be driven by safety, not administrative task completion. Audits by instructors from outside the unit are a great way to ensure comfort is not sabotaging your training effort.

Wade agreed that overcoming "the relationship" was important in optimizing training. This means knowing the guy sitting across from you is going to hold you to the standard needed to keep you safe. This might involve using a training syllabus different from the one you've flown a thousand times, with the standard maneuvers in the same order each time, to the same runway, from the same entry point.

If we are going to train to the reality of the mission, we cannot ignore emotional stress. Reichert said we forget a powerful part of IIMC incidents is the "inadvertent" part.

When we set up for IIMC training, instructors often allow trainees to prepare the aircraft before taking the controls from them so they can put on a view-limiting device. This sacrifices surprise. In a real IIMC incident, the pilot is often overcome by "instant fear," according to Reichert.

Rowles agreed that the ability to fly in IMC when you are ready is different than situations when you do not have the benefit of preparation. He suggested that a pilot's reaction to fear determines how he or she will respond to IIMC, and the idea of training to the mission extends to IIMC, meaning we should train for weather conditions in our area of operations that would most likely endanger us. Accidently flying into a thunderstorm and flying into an unexpected cloud layer in stable conditions require different response considerations.

Wade and Westbrook at Bell emphasized the importance of using full-motion simulators for IIMC training. They said TFOs should be put through the same course so they can play a role in IIMC response and increase the flight crew's chances of survival. Using the simulator, pilots can train for maneuvers or systems failures that are unacceptably dangerous or impossible to conduct in an actual aircraft.

According to George Ferito of FlightSafety international, the three most useless things in aviation are "the fuel left behind, the altitude above you and the unpracticed instrument ticket in your wallet." He said the "only substitute for experience is training."

Bryan O'Leary and Martin Scherrer of Diamond Airborne Sensing offered a final perspective on IIMC accidents. O'Leary, a former Marine Corps F/A-18 pilot, said modern equipment should help decrease the accident rate in our industry, especially in terms of IIMC/CFIT accidents. While human factors such as training, mindset and experience play a huge role in risk management, environmental intervention (i.e. changing the world around the aircrew so human errors do not cause a mishap) is also critical. O'Leary said the first few seconds of an IIMC encounter are critical. He said it is vital to consider the importance of tools such as synthetic vision, IFR certified instrumentation, in-cockpit weather information and modern avionics engineered for easier pilot interaction. Such equipment decreases the workload on the pilot and makes situational awareness more immediate, allowing the crew to concentrate on flying the aircraft and navigating to a safe piece of air. O'Leary emphasized that these benefits can only be obtained if the pilot is properly trained and remains current on the use of the equipment.

For many of us, the funding needed to install these environmental safeguards is not available. However, it was not too long ago the majority of us thought high-end thermal imagers and night vision goggles were financially unattainable. Start laying the foundation now for the tools you need in your aircraft to complement the training and experience needed to keep you and your crews safe. Talk to manufacturers, training providers and your peers so you know the next steps for your unit. There was no better place than APSA's annual conference to do just that, and I'm glad I took the opportunity to talk with the many industry experts who care about our profession.

TOO MUCH AT STAKE:
Training, Policy and Safety Work Together to Increase Mission Capability

I admit at times I have used the status of being "new" as an excuse for not performing a task as well as I should have. Usually, those around us accept this defense, with the expectation that performance will improve over time. Sometimes we can get away with this. But aviation is not one of those areas we should allow being new to justify performing to lower standards. There is simply too much at stake.

I have been pleased to see so many new aviation units forming over the past few years. Both traditional and new types of operations, such as UAS-equipped agencies, are broadening the scope of our industry. The more widespread aviation support is, the more it becomes viewed as a normal part of the public safety community. This benefits us all, as long as everything goes as expected. When things go wrong, it hurts us all.

In the mid 1990s, the U.S. saw a surge in the number of law enforcement agencies operating aircraft, mainly due to the large number of military surplus helicopters being offered to the public safety community. While the industry saw massive growth during this period, a tragic spike in the accident rate began shortly afterwards. One fatal accident occurred the day after the aircraft involved was received by the agency.

Many of those agencies are no longer in the law enforcement aviation business. An established aviation unit may be able to absorb the impact to finances and reputation that even a minor accident creates, but most new units simply cannot. When it comes to safety, we do not have time to just "figure it out as we go." This applies to any operation, whether you fly manned or unmanned aircraft. The good news is there is a way to establish this foundation so when you launch on your first mission, you will already be doing things right instead of feeling your way through the process.

Most aviators, myself included, are not particularly excited about policy manuals. However, creating one is the first step in setting up not only your SMS, but also the foundation for your entire operation.

The complaint I often hear is that writing too many policies ties the hands of the operator. "What if I need to [do this] to get the job done, but the manual says we can't do it?" The answer is to use a formal process to analyze your operation, asking questions such as, "what are you trained to do, what you are equipped to do, what are you staffed to realistically handle, and what is the scope of your operation?" This is part of risk management. You are setting the risk limits of what your unit is willing to accept beforehand so when the time comes and the situation is clouded by adrenaline, partial information, urgency and countless other human factors issues, the standards you set will protect you and your crews.

Setting such policies is a challenging first step. However, it will not only improve safety, but also the effectiveness of the rest of your operation. Consider the example of requiring a two-person crew for aerial observation operations (search, patrol, etc.). The impact on safety is obvious; however, this will also improve the unit's performance and lower costs at the same time. I recently helped an agency look at the financial impact of a two-person crew versus a single pilot. We found the unit could perform a search of a specified area using a pilot and a formally trained TFO in about half the time (53 percent less) needed for a single pilot to achieve the same results. The benefits to finances and performance are obvious.

For a new unit starting up, poor performance on calls or higher than anticipated costs can shut an operation down as surely as an accident can. There isn't time to use the "new guy" excuse before consequences start making a significant and permanent impact. Writing a good unit policy before day one of operations is critical to address all of these concerns. If you've already started, there is no time to lose.

Another critical initial step is to collect information on hazards. Before you can do this, you must set up a system for identifying and submitting hazard reports. Numerous examples of hazard reporting forms are available, including those in the *SMS Toolkit* and *Installation Guide*. I recommend the form be only one page at first. The biggest challenge will be getting employees to use the form. Your goals are to get your people to become involved in the risk management process and identify as many hazards as possible. A complicated, multi-page form will likely prevent you from meeting either objective. There must also be an option to submit the form anonymously.

Send out a survey to everyone in the unit. Again, make it one page. Ask what each person thinks are the highest risk hazards for the unit. A good question someone once suggested to me is, "What do you think will lead to our unit's next accident/incident?" In addition to asking about each hazard, ask about possible solutions.

Next, perform a gap analysis to compare your unit's actual performance with the level of performance you would like to achieve. A sample gap analysis is included in the *SMS Installation Kit,* and the Airborne Public Safety Accreditation Commission (APSAC) standards are a good resource as well.

Finally, contract for an outside audit. Numerous organizations and companies can provide this service, including APSA, APSAC (as part of the accreditation process) and commercial SMS providers. You can also have a neighboring unit or aviation operation do an audit for you. Ask them to stop by and walk through your operation with a pen and paper, writing down what they think are hazards. This outside perspective will almost always produce some important information your safety program was missing.

All of this information will do you no good if you do not process it and take action. A safety committee is instrumental in making this happen. The missing items in the gap analysis, issues brought up in the audit, answers from the surveys and any hazards that have been reported should be listed in a report to take to your safety committee. Depending on the size of your operation, the committee may include everyone. At a minimum, though, you need someone in charge of training, a safety officer, a maintenance director, an administrator and someone to represent the line-level positions (pilots, TFOs, medics, crew chiefs, UAS operators, etc.).

> "The more widespread aviation support is, the more it becomes viewed as a normal part of the public safety community. This benefits us all, as long as everything goes as expected. When things go wrong, it hurts us all."

The committee should review all of the hazards and decide the associated risk. Some will have a high-risk score, and that's where you should direct your attention at first. In the beginning, your unit will have limited time and resources, so you want to concentrate your efforts where you will make the most significant impact on safety. Without this process, you will just be making guesses and wasting time and money. In the committee, develop the mitigation strategies that will reduce the risk in each of the hazards you choose to target.

Every mitigation strategy requires some element of training. It is not enough to tell people what hazards to avoid; you need to show them how to avoid them. Too often, our safety programs are limited to listing the hazards in emails, posters and reminders. You've seen them: "Be safe," "Don't make a bad decision on weather," "Be careful not to hit a bird," "Fatigue is dangerous." While these statements are well intended, they fail to inform us how to accomplish each suggestion. This is usually because there is not a good working relationship between safety and training. Every time you come up with a plan to reduce the risk in a hazard, think about the training element. An eight-hour class or hour-long training flight won't be required every time. The training element may be adequately served by a required reading, roll call training or detailed email. If you forget this part of the process, your SMS will be a toothless tiger.

Safety related training should also address operational needs. Let's look at the two-person crew example. If we are going to require the use of TFOs on certain missions, we need to think about their training. For TFOs to be an effective means of lowering risk on a flight, they must be trained. That training will also make them more effective in the aircraft, leading to more successful missions. A highly effective TFO will help lower operational costs by shortening the time required for a successful outcome and reducing risk, such as the likelihood of costly accidents and incidents.

What's described here is a perfect example of SMS—training, policy and safety working together to increase mission capability, lower costs and increase safety. And it can be achieved by focusing your energy right at the beginning. Sometimes, we think the professionalism of an operation is defined by being established in the industry through a history of successful missions. I disagree. Your new unit can be extremely professional from the first day of operations if you take the time to set up the framework that will allow you to safely complete missions successfully. You simply cannot afford not to; there is too much at stake to let it all ride on the excuse of being "new."

TACTICAL PROFILES & CAPABILITIES:
Aircraft, Mission Equipment, Crew Composition & Training

For many years, I sought answers that don't exist. I wanted to know the specific numbers for the best altitude to search for a suspect or manage a pursuit. Was it 500 feet—1,000 feet? I wanted to know the correct speed for the orbit. And what direction should I turn? Like many others, I wanted to be the best I could be at my job. I wanted to know the perfect flight profile to catch every bad guy I had the opportunity to pursue. However, if I asked 10 people the same question, I received 10 different answers.

So, being new, I did what those around me did and figured it must be correct. As far as finding bad guys went—the lower the better, right? As I started thinking about flight safety more, I asked the same questions and received the same ambiguous answers. As far as safety goes—the higher the better, right? One thing was clear, most of us felt our own opinion on the best profile was gospel, and anyone doing anything different was either reckless or timid.

The answers to most questions in public safety aviation are not universal numbers. What is the perfect flight profile? Whatever profile you have trained for that gives you the best tactical advantage for the task at hand.

We all fly in different aircraft, in different environments, with different equipment. We also fly on different missions, from missing persons to suspect searches, firefighting, surveillance and hoist rescues. All of these factors determine our best profile. One altitude and orbit direction may be ideal for a mission in the morning, and a completely different profile may be ideal in the afternoon. If we limit ourselves to one profile, we will frequently miss the opportunity to maximize the capability of our aviation assets.

The priority of a public safety pilot is to provide a stable platform for the crew to do its work. This applies to searches with cameras or unaided eyes, hoist operations and UAS flights.

The airborne platform should provide the maximum search area and options for searching between buildings and other obstructions. In general, higher is better. The limit is the optical capability needed to search for the target in question, depending on whether you are using the eyes, binoculars or a camera system. The required optics-range will depend on the size of the target. If we are searching for a vehicle, we can select a higher altitude to increase stability, viewing area and angles. If the mission shifts from a vehicle to a person, we can decrease altitude as needed to adjust for the range of our optics.

I was once on a ride-along with a crew responding to an armed robbery suspect in a backyard. Once on scene, we orbited at a high speed at 300 to 400 feet. For approximately 60 percent of the orbit, the suspect was blocked from our view by the second floor of a building. After a few orbits, the pilot climbed approximately 200 feet, making the suspect visible in most of the orbit. Our airspeed also decreased, and the aircraft attitude settled down considerably.

Airspeed also depends on the aircraft and mission objective. Higher altitudes allow more options for different airspeeds in all categories of aircraft. Slower airspeeds allow for a longer search in particular areas, which is important because we must stop our scan for at least two to four seconds to allow our eyes to focus at the level of detail we need to find most targets.

The need to scan slowly may have to be balanced with the need to search an entire area from as many angles as possible, which requires a higher airspeed. Generally, hovering is the most effective choice only when we know exactly where our target is, it is not moving and we have only one good viewing angle.

In our industry, we often use the term orbit to describe our operational profile. Do we need to orbit all the time? No. Many other options are effective, including grids, routes, creeping lines, expanding squares or circles, and others. We can adjust our orbit to eliminate blind spots near buildings. Sometimes, it's effective to shift to one side and move the target area completely outside the orbit. We can still search the target area with a camera system while a suspect thinks we have departed and it is safe to move.

> "The correct orbit direction is based on your aircraft, mission equipment, number of crewmembers and, most importantly, training."

One of the most controversial topics in public safety aviation is whether you should orbit to the pilot or TFO side. I was once cursed at for even bringing up the question. But as with the questions above, I do not believe there is one right answer.

The correct orbit direction is based on your aircraft, mission equipment, number of crewmembers and, most importantly, training. Both options present hazards. Both directions create blind spots. Both pull a pilot's attention away from the flight path to either the ground or the TFO's monitor. We must take the time to honestly look at the hazards involved in the profile we choose and talk about ways to mitigate them. If we think our choice is ideal, and there are no hazards to discuss, we are blind to our blind spots.

Turning to the pilot side because the TFO is not capable of working the call without assistance from the pilot is not a good reason to turn that direction. This usually indicates the TFO has not been trained properly or does not have the aptitude for the job. Turning to the TFO side because the officer cannot work the camera system well and needs to constantly look out the window is not a good reason to turn that direction. Again, this is either a training or aptitude problem and should not be masked with a tactical band-aid. Pick a profile that gives you the best tactical advantage based on your aircraft, cockpit setup, mission type and equipment, and train for the advantages and disadvantages the profile offers.

So what does all this have to do with safety? The optimum flight profile on any mission mitigates risk as much as reasonably practical. We must be no lower than required by the mission, no slower than needed to scan properly, and we should be properly training aircrew members so we do not have to choose less-than-ideal profiles to make up for lack of capability.

With a profile that maximizes our aerial viewpoint and equipment capabilities, we will have more operational success, including bringing the equipment and crew home safely for the next flight.

PERSONAL PROTECTIVE EQUIPMENT:
The Modern Aviator's Suit of Armor

As a teenager, I remember standing at the bus stop freezing. It was usually about an hour before sunrise, and I was lucky if the temperature was above zero. I wasn't cold because my parents had failed to provide me with warm winter clothes; I was cold because I wasn't wearing the clothes. The hat messed up my hair, so it was stuffed in my coat pocket. A zipped-up coat made a teenage boy look like a wimp, so I left it unzipped, which surely impressed the ninth grade ladies standing nearby. And this was the era when it was cool to have giant holes ripped in the knees of one's pants, so frostbitten legs were the price of looking "in" and stylish. Despite having all the appropriate clothing, I remained ironically uncool. And frozen.

Public safety aviation will always carry risk, even when performed in the most professional manner possible. The risks include thermal injuries from fire and trauma from objects entering the cabin or the dynamics of impacting the ground in an accident. Fortunately, we have effective options for reducing the severity of injury. But in some cases, financial constraints mean we lack the appropriate personal protective equipment (PPE). Or, as in the case when I refused to wear my warm clothes as a teenager, incidents occur because we choose not to utilize PPE despite having it available.

Is the problem simply that we do not understand what we should be wearing? Is it a lack of agency leadership requiring that standard PPE be utilized? While these may sometimes be the core issues, it is too narrow a focus if we want more widespread protection for our friends and peers.

I recently spoke with my unit's director of maintenance and asked him about his take on PPE. He suggested that even though maintenance professionals have PPE available and understand how it works, often the question is, "When should I use it?" While a mechanic typically knows the PPE requirements for most jobs, sometimes work may involve chemicals or processes that are new or rarely used. If safety information, such as material safety data sheets, is outdated or unavailable, even the most professional technician may be left guessing about proper PPE use. Again, it is not a lack of desire to be safe; we may just be failing to answer the right questions.

PPE should not be thought of as individual items. Each piece is part of one protective system that requires multiple pieces of gear in order to work effectively. Think of your PPE as a suit of armor. The armor historically worn by knights on the battlefield was nearly invincible, but it was being struck at the weak points that caused the warriors to lose to their enemies.

The preferred weak point was at one of the joints where moving parts came together, such as the shoulders, knees, neck or visor. The seat of the pants was only lightly armored for horse riding. Some knights, either due to lack of finances, weather conditions or to facilitate travel, chose to wear only body plates and headgear and not arm or leg armor. Partially armored knights were more easily maimed, which was good enough for an opponent. For the less chivalrous warrior, an option to best an opponent, often to collect a ransom, was to wait for him to remove his armor when his guard was down.

During my research on traditional armor, it struck me how many similarities there were with the modern aviator's PPE. The weakest point in our protection is often the joints. The point where the flight suit meets the hands, feet and neck is often exposed because we either wear those parts of our suit improperly or not at all.

We all know flight suits are fire resistant. In the most recent APSA safety survey, we asked what PPE our members wear during flights. As might be expected, 91 percent responded they wear a flight suit and 90 percent said they wear leather boots. However, only 82 percent said they wear flight gloves.

Aviators often forget that if sleeve cuffs are left open (sleeves rolled up, no gloves, etc.), fire and heat will find that weak point and cause harm far beyond just the exposed skin. It is a failure point for the whole system, not just the hands. Just like for those knights who wore torso armor but nothing on the legs or arms, the protection offered by the flight suit is dependent on the proper use of the whole fire protection system.

Another weak point is the space between the flight suit and the skin. If the flight suit is too tight, it cannot function properly. If synthetic material without fire resistant qualities occupies the space between the suit and body, the system will allow the materials to melt into the skin instead of protecting from thermal injury as designed.

Just as it did for knights, partial protection may save your life, but you will be left with injuries that will prevent you from doing what you need to do to survive. The fire protection system we are wearing is not just for the post-crash fire. We may need the system to help us deal with an in-flight fire, as was the case for the pilot of a Cessna 172RG on Sept. 28, 2010. During the flight, a fire started behind the instrument panel and quickly spread to the floor. The pilot was unable to manipulate the fuel selector because it was too hot. The flames under the instrument panel began to melt his shoes, making it difficult to operate the rudder pedals, and then started his lower pants legs on fire. (See NTSB report CEN10LA572 for more.)

On Dec. 4, 2010, a BK 117 was on final approach to land when a wiring harness in the cabin gave in to seven years of chaffing and caught on fire, emitting smoke and flames. Another crewmember was able to use an extinguisher to put the fire out while the pilot continued landing. (See NTSB report ERA11IA091.)

After we land a disabled aircraft, we still have to remove ourselves, crewmembers and passengers from a structure that may be on fire. Depending on the landing, we may be on our side, in an unlit area, or in rough terrain. All these factors mean it may not be easy to escape. Removing seatbelts, grabbing equipment, assisting crewmembers and other tasks conducted in fire conditions will be easier if we have our complete thermal protection system in place. Remember, you will be performing these tasks with whatever gear you had on when the emergency started.

It can be difficult to use the controls on camera systems and small keyboards in flight while wearing gloves if you are a tactical flight officer or other aircrew member. If you are a crew chief, you may need a different glove than that used during hoist operations. But it should not be an all or nothing equation. Wear the gloves as often as possible, only taking them off when absolutely necessary. Often, the problem is that we have not purchased the right size or gone through the process of fitting them using warm water.

Worse than improperly fitted gloves is an improperly fitted helmet. Knights wore helmets that were effective against weapon impact but not known for being comfortable or easy to see through. But there is no arguing the value of a helmet in protecting the skull against impact forces in an accident.

Like fire-resistant clothing, helmets are not just for aircraft accidents. Recently, a bird broke the canopy of a law enforcement helicopter working a call at night. The bird struck the pilot, lacerating his face, breaking his nose and damaging one eye. The pilot was not wearing a helmet. According to APSA survey respondents, 44 percent said that they had experienced between one and three bird strikes in the last three years, and an additional 12 percent reported more than three. In those strikes, 16 percent of the birds entered the cockpit.

A helmet can also prevent long-term hearing damage, as long as it is fitted and adjusted correctly. A properly fitted helmet provides a solid seal around the ear and balances the weight of the equipment, including night vision goggles, on the center of the head to reduce neck strain and hot spots. We have all worn a helmet that didn't fit correctly or had scuffed visors. It is a miserable experience.

Instructors should check the volume settings of their aircrew members' helmets, especially for the new folks. Abnormally high settings often mean the helmet needs to be adjusted. Frequent discomfort when wearing NVGs or a large amount of counterweight on the back can also indicate improper fit. Work with your helmet manufacturer or dealer for tips on fitting and adjusting.

Aviators do not have time to don fire protection or helmets during an event requiring them. In most cases, if PPE is not on when the emergency starts, it will not be on when it ends. The same can be said for survival gear. In the APSA Safety Survey, 24 percent of respondents said they wore a survival vest always, and 24 percent wore one sometimes. The number of respondents indicating their vest incorporated a survival vest and emergency oxygen was about the same.

Survival vests are not just for flight over sparse terrain. Following an accident, we may find ourselves pinned in the aircraft or unable to move far from it. Even if rescue takes 15-20 minutes, the items in our vest or within arm's reach can make a huge difference in survivability. We must be able to provide immediate emergency medical aid to our crew and ourselves. For most aircraft accidents, that means stopping blood loss and treating thermal injuries and broken bones. We also need to be able to summon assistance using handheld radios, personal locator beacons, etc., if the aircraft radios and beacons are not working. What we carry beyond that depends on the environment in which we operate.

Water survival gear is not just for flights beyond gliding distance from shore. On Aug. 16, 2012, a Jabiru J230 was conducting a public use flight in northern New York over hilly and densely forested terrain. At 6,500 feet, the engine lost power and the propeller flew from the aircraft. Even at that altitude, the most suitable landing place was a lake. (See NTSB report ERA12TA542.)

In many of the areas we fly, water may be the best choice for a forced landing. If we do choose to land in water, exiting the aircraft upside down and underwater will not be a good time to put on a life preserver. If it wasn't on before the emergency, it will not be on after the emergency.

An EC-145 was flying to a landing site to pick up a patient at night near Ft. Myers, FL, on Aug. 17, 2009. One of the medics was surprised to see what he thought were raindrops on the side window when suddenly the aircraft was in the water, sinking and rolling over. The pilot and medics managed to egress the helicopter, but their survival vests were still in the aircraft. Fortunately, the fire department realized the aircraft was overdue and had a boat nearby begin a search. The crew was rescued 20 minutes after the crash. That might not seem long, but anyone who has tread water in a flight suit would disagree. The crew's saving grace was that the shallow water allowed them to stand on the submerged aircraft. (See NTSB report ERA09LA464.)

In public safety aviation, unpredictability is one of the things that attracts the exceptional types of people I love working with. Our workday can go from boring to historic in a heartbeat with no warning. We tend to think we will only need our suit of armor in certain, specific events that rarely happen. In reality, all of our PPE composes a system that is only as strong as the weakest link. The system is providing benefit to our wellbeing 100 percent of the time if it is used properly.

So "when do we need our PPE?" If the answer only connects specific pieces of equipment to specific events (usually the most catastrophic ones), we tend to focus on the low likelihood of those events. But each piece of equipment has multiple uses, some of which are in play nearly all the time. A focus on separate PPE items ignores the fact they are individual pieces of a larger system.

We never know when fate will pick a fight with us. I do not want to be caught in the greatest battle of my life wishing I hadn't left my suit of armor in the locker.

MINIMIZE RISKS AND INCREASE FIXED-WING SAFETY:
Overcoming IIMC, Stall/Spin, LOC & More

I had been flying law enforcement missions in a helicopter for five years before I had the opportunity to work those same missions from an airplane. I was not too concerned about it, because I had been an airplane pilot for longer than I had been flying helicopters. I figured the combination of these two experiences would make flying law enforcement missions in an airplane a no-brainer. I was wrong.

Many aspects of law enforcement aviation are universal, whether the aircraft is an airplane, helicopter, powered parachute or other flying machine. Similarly, any pilot in a particular category of aircraft needs to be proficient at certain skills, no matter what part of the industry they are in, from airline pilot to bush pilot. However, there are some aspects of doing law enforcement from the air in an airplane that are specific and need targeted attention, training and experience.

According to the APSA law enforcement accident database in 2014, 25 accidents have occurred in fixed-wing aircraft since 1998. Nineteen people were killed in those accidents. Controlled flight into terrain (CFIT) was a more common causal factor than any other, with eight incidents total. Of those CFIT accidents, five were directly attributed to inadvertent flight into instrument meteorological conditions (IIMC). In these cases, 12 people were killed, which is 63 percent of the fixed-wing fatalities in the last 15 years. This category was similar to rotorcraft accidents in our industry around the same time, in that IIMC was killing us more than anything else. What is different is that most of the fixed-wing accidents involved instrument-rated aircraft with instrument-rated pilots.

AIR SUPPORT SAFETY

Prior to looking at these numbers, I felt more comfortable flying in marginal weather in the agency airplane than I did in the helicopter because both the aircraft and I were rated for instrument flight. The problem is that I was trained for planned, not inadvertent, instrument flight.

According to the Aircraft Owners and Pilots Association Nall Report, an instrument-rated pilot is occupying at least one of the two front seats in 46 percent of weather-related fatal accidents. Looking at the information available, that percentage is even higher in our industry when it comes to fixed-wing IIMC accidents.

Instrument training is part of the answer to this problem, but not the complete answer. APSA has published inadvertent instrument training recommendations and posted a video presentation on its website to address the other half of the solution. It is vital that we do not let our mission and faith in instrument capabilities draw us into inadvertent IMC flight.

The second highest occurrence category in fatal fixed-wing law enforcement accidents is the stall/spin. These accidents have claimed the lives of seven aviators. Low-level stall/spin accidents are a common killer throughout the fixed-wing world, often occurring during the landing and takeoff phases of flight.

We prepare for these scenarios in primary flight training with stern lessons on refraining from turning back to the runway if the engine is lost after takeoff, the importance of flying a stabilized approach, and the dangers of overcorrecting or getting "crossed controls" during turns in the pattern. The vast majority of law enforcement stall/spin accidents, however, occur during missions when the pilot is orbiting or making turns in a search pattern. Often, the pilot is alone, flying the aircraft and performing the mission. These are a different set of circumstances and conditions than those we address in training and with operational procedures.

One of the most powerful means of lowering risk in this scenario is to have a trained and capable TFO aboard handling the mission. This unloads the pilot of mission tasking, allowing him or her to concentrate on flying while simultaneously increasing efficiency and safety in other areas through crew resource management.

None of the stall/spin accident records I encountered indicated the crew was using an external camera or thermal imager. The flight profile when using camera systems tends to carry less risk of these types of accidents due to higher altitudes and airspeeds and wider flight patterns.

Another risk management option would be to have a checklist for setting up the cockpit for the mission before arriving on scene. This would remove the need to complete those tasks while simultaneously establishing the aircraft in a mission flight profile.

Spin training is an ideal solution to this issue, but if it is not an option, limited training on stall/spin recognition and preventive recovery from a mission profile should be considered. After all, in most cases, our operational altitudes will severely limit our ability to recover from a spin. Many of the accidents I looked at involved cases where the airplane did not even make a full turn before impact. Prevention is the best medicine. The scenarios used during this training should include both traditional takeoff and landing events, as well as mission-specific law enforcement flight profiles. Such training should only be performed with an instructor who is trained and proficient and from altitudes that will allow for safe recovery if the maneuver is not performed as planned.

Rounding out the top three categories of fixed-wing law enforcement accidents is loss of control (LOC) on landing. These accidents are a mix of crosswind, tailwind and ground loop incidents. Although I am sure there have been more, there are six accident reports involving law enforcement airplanes in the last 15 years in this category. Fortunately, there were no fatalities.

When discussing this issue with others, it quickly becomes apparent that we tend to assume a licensed commercial pilot can handle any landing within the unit's established weather limitations. This assumption leads to less emphasis during training. Compounding the issue is the natural desire to conduct training flights when the weather is calm, usually early in the day. I am certainly guilty of scheduling my training flights only when the sun is within 15 degrees of the horizon and the windsock is predicted to be hanging straight down.

Unfortunately, the nature of our business is such that we are often needed when the conditions are least favorable. I do not recommend training in conditions beyond unit limits. However, if you are expected to fly missions when there is a 15-knot crosswind, train once in a while in those conditions.

Flight instructors should be aware that the highest number of fixed-wing training accidents in our industry is also LOC on landing. When training in these conditions, have a zero tolerance policy on stabilized approaches flown down the extended centerline. That is what we train our pilots to do, as opposed to trying to salvage an unstable approach from 20 degrees left of course. Go around and do it right.

An additional note on landing accidents: A trained TFO or second pilot reduces the risk in this category tremendously. The availability of a second crewmember who can read checklists, confirm aircraft configuration or take care of last minute mission-related tasks can make a huge difference in safety during the landing phase of flight.

The last factor I would like to mention is related to pilots themselves. Law enforcement pilots involved in incidents tend to have more total flight time than the average general aviation pilot. When it comes to make and model time, however, the numbers are significantly different. According to the National Transportation Safety Board, public-use category pilots involved in an accident have on average 3,500 hours of total time but only 300 in make and model. Unfortunately, this category includes industries other than law enforcement, so the context of the data is not perfect. Still, we can see how total time can be an incomplete indicator of pilot proficiency in law enforcement operations if the operator is relatively new to the aircraft. It is time spent performing law enforcement operations in make and model that has the biggest impact on safety. This phenomena is another that is common to both rotorcraft and fixed-wing pilots.

Other hazards and risks are associated with fixed-wing law enforcement aviation. However, if we take the time to address the three categories listed above, we can work on the factors causing 75 percent of accidents and 90 percent of fatalities. Experience flying airplanes for a long time, be it 747s or F-22s, or conducting law enforcement in another category of aircraft, does not give anyone the full skillset needed to safely engage in law enforcement flying in a fixed-wing aircraft. The three accident categories discussed here all have unique aspects, specific to our line of work, which need to be addressed in order to perform with the lowest risk possible.

CLOSE ENCOUNTERS:
Simulator Training is Not
Just for Emergencies

There are no new ways to crash an aircraft." Anyone who has been a pilot for more than a week has heard this at least once. Flight safety experts around the world use it in presentations and articles with little or no disagreement. However, it generally has little impact on our safety efforts because we don't expand on it. How can this knowledge help us?

First, we should recognize the means of crashing aircraft have not changed because the major hazards causing those accidents have also remained constant. Hazards linked to the weather, human biology and the laws of nature are beyond our control. In order to address them, we must continue to develop training and safety tools to control how we interact with them.

Second, we must build on our strategies for addressing the aviation challenges we can control. The training and safety methods we have developed over a century of flight have lowered the accident rate to where it is today. If we want to decrease it further, we must do more.

Perhaps there are no new ways of crashing aircraft. But there are new ways to keep us from crashing them.

One of the methods of correcting age-old ways to crash aircraft is using flight simulators. No, flight simulators are not new, but they have come a long way. My first logbook entry in a simulator was in 1991, and I still remember sitting in a smelly box listening to the drone of electrically powered gauges as I moved instrument needles with a set of squeaky controls. My view outside the cockpit was the outdated wallpaper in an FBO's windowless simulator/weather station/flight planning/storage room.

Around that time, programs such as Microsoft's Flight Simulator series started showing up for home computers. For those of us in public safety aviation, the advancement of flight simulation technology largely left us behind at that level of sophistication. Unless we had a background in the military or the airlines, most of us did not have access to advanced simulators.

My own experience kept my expectations low when I was given the chance to fly in a new single-engine helicopter simulator in 2012. As I stepped into the full motion, 240-degree view, full-cockpit simulator with realistic audio and control feedback, I was anticipating an easygoing exercise in "centering the needles." After a challenging, educational, eye-opening, physically and psychologically stressful session, my perception of simulator-based training's limitations was changed permanently.

Yes, modern simulation-based training in the context of public safety aviation is relatively new. It is new in both capability and its growing impact on our industry. And it is a new way to keep from crashing aircraft.

One important element of IIMC training is the inadvertent part. The sudden and unplanned entry into instrument conditions creates powerful mental and physiological challenges, such as loss of situational awareness, vertigo and plain old fear. When we train in an actual aircraft for instrument flight, we see the instructor pull out the blinders ahead of time. He or she then gives us a minute to put them on while taking the controls. I know I am guilty of dragging out the process so I can take a last glance at everything and make sure I am stable on the controls before announcing I "have the aircraft" again. Often, we are even given the chance to dial in the frequencies and approach procedures we will need before putting on the "foggles." Mother Nature is not so kind.

> "Often, we are given the chance to dial in the frequencies and approach procedures we will need before putting on the 'foggles.' Mother Nature is not so kind."

Additionally, even the best view limiting devices do not always block out all outside views. The ground passing through the chin bubble on a helicopter may seem like a minor issue, until it is taken away and you realize how much it was helping you maintain situational awareness. Most view limiting devices in the aircraft we train in, especially helicopters, give us the equivalent of approximately 0.25-mile visibility. The difference between a quarter mile and true 0/0 weather conditions can be significant.

Finally, how far do we let a student take an aircraft outside of a normal flight profile before taking it back from him or her? In a real aircraft, we cannot afford to let a student take it far enough to truly illustrate the lethality of the path they might be on before the instructor steps in. There is something intrinsically educational about popping out of the clouds to find the horizon in a location nowhere near where you were certain you would see it.

A modern simulator can allow us to train for an IIMC encounter in a manner that we cannot achieve safely in the aircraft. When I climbed into a modern simulator for the first time in 2012, the instructor coyly diverted my attention to an object outside the cockpit while I was in a turn. Suddenly, he flipped the IIMC switch and I was in zero visibility conditions in a 30-degree bank. It was a perfect simulation of a distracted law enforcement pilot entering the clouds in an orbit. Looking for my trusty bit of ground through the chin bubble, I saw nothing but white mist. While I am an instrument rated pilot and instrument flight instructor, it took everything I had to level the aircraft and climb through it.

In the air-conditioned safety of the simulator, I found my heart beating against my rib cage and unwelcome beads of sweat on my forehead. Confessing to the instructor the difficulty I had in maintaining control, he assured me it was normal. He later informed me the majority of his first time IIMC students crash within one to two minutes, regardless of experience or ratings. After a few sessions, my nerves improved, but the most important lesson I took away was reconfirmation of the fact that avoiding IIMC in the first place is critical if I wanted to see retirement.

Simulators offer us more than just IIMC training. Mechanical failures that would be impossible or too dangerous to perform in the aircraft can be simulated. Examples include the ability to train for governor failures, engine surging, abnormal instrument readings or failures (e.g. rotor tach failure and various oil pressure and temp indications), flight control malfunctions, tail rotor failures and countless others.

In my simulator experience, I was able to play with the throttle settings following high and low governor failures, which thankfully I had never experienced in real life. I even landed the aircraft with a high-side governor failure. Later, we simulated a tail rotor failure in a hover, which was eye opening to say the least, as it was first initiated without warning. The actual settings needed to respond to each were somewhat different than what I'd imagined they would be.

Many of these procedures seem straightforward enough when reading the POH or discussing them on the ground. When they happen in the aircraft, however, aspects of each situation that were never previously considered come into play. Even if those unanticipated items are small, they take up time and divert attention from critical tasks, which can delay or alter the required response.

For example, during one of my simulator flights the instructor spontaneously illuminated the cargo door light—a simple and benign little yellow light. The light is so insignificant, I'd never thought too much about what I would do if it popped on in flight. A reminder of several fatal accidents involving equipment flying out of unsecured doors prompted a permanent adjustment of my perspective. The fire light was next, which was coupled with the various indicators of an actual engine fire—followed by another significant shift in perspective.

Sim training is not just for the emergencies we cannot do in an actual aircraft. Simulators also allow us to perform core emergency procedures without wear and tear or potential damage to our machines. For many public safety aviation units, one training accident can put the unit out of business for a long time, even permanently. Engine failures and other emergency procedures can be carried all the way to the ground without concern about aircraft damage. You can crash a sim all day long and, fortunately, there is no simulated visit from the FAA or NTSB.

Want to practice an emergency procedure from a mission flight profile? Orbiting an urban area at low altitude in the middle of the night is a likely profile for a real-life emergency. It is also a lousy profile for engine failure practice. Sometimes, a practice emergency procedure turns into a real emergency and a real accident. In a simulator, we can practice these procedures from realistic mission profiles over actual mission terrain without worrying about crashing in the process.

How about training as a crew? Often, we train with a pilot and instructor in the aircraft and leave the TFO at the hangar. On actual missions and in real emergencies, it is the TFO in the seat next to the pilot. An untrained TFO is a waste of what could otherwise be a lifesaving resource in an emergency. Most modern simulators have full cockpits that allow you to train as a crew and develop your CRM skills. Many new simulators also have law enforcement equipment, such as thermal imagers, included as part of the simulation.

The modern simulator is one tool to prevent us from encountering one of the age-old ways to crash an aircraft. In the past, the availability and capabilities of simulators for typical public safety-type aircraft were limited. That is no longer the case. Modern simulators can offer critical training focused on human factors, realistic mission profiles and mechanical errors that simply cannot be done safely, if at all, in an actual aircraft.

THE EDGE:
Training for LOC Scenarios

Training to be a trainer is, in my opinion, the highest form of aviation professionalism. Learning to become a good flight instructor is the most difficult thing I've ever done as a pilot. After many years as a CFI, I am still working on it.

Being an instructor is filled with difficult balances. How much should you tell students, and how much should you make them figure out on their own? When does a student need to be pushed a little harder in the same direction, and when is a different approach needed? How far should you let them mess up a maneuver, and when should you take the controls?

Questions like these do not come with clear answers. The ambiguity has led to many training accidents, including one in which I was involved as an instructor. Despite the significant number of training related incidents, the advice given to new instructors is still vague and ineffective: "Students will try to kill you; don't let them do it."

If we look up training accident reports, they usually end with a statement suggesting the student did something he or she shouldn't have or failed to do something, and the flight instructor didn't correct

PAVING THE WAY

P = People • The pilot must ask, "Am I ready for this trip?" in terms of experience, currency, physical, and emotional condition. IMSAFE: Illness, Medicine, Stress, Alcohol, Fatigue/Food, Emotion

A = Aircraft • What about the aircraft? What limitations will the aircraft impose upon the trip?

V = Environment • Weather, Terrain, Airport, Airspace, Nighttime

E = External Pressures • External pressures are influences external to the flight that create a sense of pressure to complete a flight.

the error in time. The normal response to such a conclusion is to tell the student to do it differently next time and the instructor to stop the error more quickly if it happens again. Still not very helpful.

With the exception of actual engine or aircraft component failures, nearly all training accidents are due to loss of control (LOC). If we compare the probable cause statement above to the definition of LOC, we see two of the three elements align nicely: 1. The aircraft doesn't go where the pilot wants it to go. 2. The aircraft goes where the pilot doesn't want it to go. 3. It is unexpected.

It is the third item that holds the key to so many training related incidents. Whatever happened, it was unexpected. This seems counterintuitive because our training flights are usually more scripted and controlled than a typical public safety sortie.

When we think of LOC incidents in general, we often think of the aircraft's performance envelope. Normally, we are taught where the limit is and told to stop doing what we are doing when we reach it. But sometimes the edge of the envelope is difficult to detect. We may not know where the limit is until we have crossed it. Even if we can see the edge, if we are approaching it at too fast a rate, we will not be able to stop our momentum and reverse the trend in time.

Our understanding of the performance envelope also tends to be fatally limited to a focus on aircraft capabilities. Aircraft control involves staying within the performance limitations of all the PAVE model elements: pilot-in-command, aircraft, environment and external pressures.

Human performance varies from day to day based on health, fatigue, experience, etc. Environmental elements, such as weather, lighting, terrain, etc., influence control limitations. External pressures can have a big impact. Ever felt rushed to complete training because of travel or work schedules? How about the pressure of a training flight being an evaluation that could impact your career? These elements should be included in a training-specific flight risk assessment tool (FRAT). Often, they are not considered, leaving the flight's performance envelope undefined.

Training LOC scenarios are further complicated by communication issues between the student and instructor and aircraft and crew. Crew resource management is different during a training flight. The instructor is typically not your usual aircrew partner. You may be familiar with how the folks you work with communicate, but it is different with an instructor. People are generally not as comfortable asking questions during a training flight, despite the instructor saying, "Let me know if you have any questions." This is especially true if the flight is associated with an evaluation of some sort. The salty, crass, stern flight instructor will rarely receive any feedback that isn't forced.

Communication during training flights can also be affected by pilot nerves. Or the pilot may not ask the instructor a question because of lack of experience. Training is the process of learning something we did not previously know. Pilots learning a new skill will often not know what to ask and say they have no questions. This can lead to an instructor making dangerous assumptions.

The Kung Fu legend Bruce Lee was known for incredible speed. He used a technique called "sticky hands" that gave him reflexes that were truly quicker than the eye could see. Closing the gap with opponents, he would lay his hands or forearms on their arms, allowing him to feel their attacks and respond before his eyes could detect the move and process a response.

In the aircraft, we establish communication with the machine through the same technique. We touch the controls and interpret what we feel. When a flight instructor takes their hands off the controls, his or her reflexes are severely impacted. One of the lessons new instructors have to master is how to guard the controls without being so heavy on them that the student cannot learn.

We also communicate with the aircraft by listening and watching what the machine and instruments are doing. Inaccurate assumptions driven by crew communication issues can lead instructors to stop listening to the aircraft—they think the student is doing it, without question. When a problem arises, the instructor's response is delayed as they reestablish aircraft communication.

Train how you fight, and fight how you train. We've all heard quotes like this countless times. Yet when we train, the maneuvers and flight profiles often do not resemble our normal activities. We fly differently when we are in training. Our cockpit and avionics are set up differently, we carry different gear on the aircraft, or we wear different equipment and PPE in "training mode." Aircrews who normally fly at night may be given refresher training during the day. Or circumstances may require that we fly aircraft other than our agency machines, with different instrument panels, equipment configurations and weights.

With all of this working against us, it's no wonder we have incidents. We cannot stop training, but we also have to do something different to lower the number of accidents than tell people to "be careful." During every training flight, remember to do the following:

> 1) Establish the actual performance envelope for the day. Look at all performance limiting factors by completing a training FRAT that covers all PAVE model elements.

2) Spend more time briefing flights and maneuvers. Even during refresher training for an established pilot, do not rely on asking, "Do you have any questions?" Brief the flight, including maneuver criteria, with everyone.

3) Conduct training flights that are not evaluations. We have to have evaluations. We do not have to have them all the time. Give crew an opportunity to fly with an instructor, ask questions and learn, instead of always performing for a test.

4) Set criteria for starting and aborting maneuvers before reaching the edge of the performance envelope. This is not just for engine failure training. For every maneuver, set a window for starting and criteria for aborting. The abort point should be well before the edge of the performance envelope. Stop the maneuver when the student is doing it wrong; don't let it continue to get worse so you can show how good you are at saving a bad performance.

5) Base criteria for maneuvers on actual, real life scenarios. Why are you doing the maneuver? How do you want it done? Stop the maneuver when it exceeds those limits. Write the scenarios and limits down so they can be covered in the briefing.

6) Train with operational factors in place—same uniform, cockpit setup, etc. Sometimes you cannot make a training flight 100 percent the same as an operational flight, but do not let that keep you from trying.

7) Train the trainer. It is not easy to train. "Knowing" something is different than "teaching" it. Flight instruction is a business that should be conducted by trained flight instructors. Maintaining control of the aircraft and what the student is

doing, while allowing them to learn, is a difficult thing to master. Instructors need to be motivated to teach others. They have to have people skills in order to minimize communication challenges. Instructors can learn much from other instructors if afforded the opportunity to attend events specifically focused on teaching techniques.

WEATHER SAFETY FOR PUBLIC SAFETY AVIATORS

In the past, when conducting weather planning for my public safety flights, I was a member of a group of seemingly forgotten aviators. We are the ones that hit the "zoom in" button as much as we can on weather maps because we need a look at the local area, not an entire region of the country. We are the ones who lower the winds aloft observation levels as low as they can go, and they are still higher than we intend to fly. We are the aviators who look at conditions at two airports and wonder what awaits us between them, because our job requires going to the blank spots among the weather reports. Weather services seemed to be designed for other kinds of folks, not us.

If you work in North America, you may know of a unique weather product that was designed for the type of flying many of us typically conduct—the HEMS Weather Tool available on the NOAA Aviation Weather Center (AWC) website. Over the past few years, I have noticed that the resource is a common sight on public safety aviation unit ready room computer monitors. And for good reason.

To find out more about the weather tool, I interviewed Bruce Carmichael and Arnaud Dumont from the National Center for Atmospheric Research (NCAR), Rex Alexander, past president of the National EMS Pilots Association (NEMSPA), Mike Bettwy and Kevin Stone from the National Oceanic Atmospheric Administration (NOAA) and Steve Abelman, manager of FAA's Aviation Weather Research Team. I don't think too many people will be surprised to hear the project was started in response to the unacceptably high number of weather related accidents within the helicopter air ambulance (HAA) community, formerly referred to as HEMS.

Around 2006, the FAA came to NCAR with a proposal to develop a weather depiction resource that would give HAA helicopter crews the information they needed to bring down the accident rate. They realized HAA operations were often conducted far from official weather reporting points. HAA flights were also being flown at altitudes below the levels depicted in most weather resources. Traditional sources were simply not meeting the safety requirements of an industry struggling to lower weather related accidents. FAA and NCAR wisely brought in industry experts, such as NEMSPA's Alexander, to help create an effective solution.

As mentioned, HAA operations are often conducted in areas without traditional weather reporting sources, so the group looked at pulling weather information from all available outlets. To do this, they decided to incorporate non-traditional weather sources, such as the Department of Transportation, universities, airlines, etc. This information helped fill the gaps between the traditional reporting sources. Additionally, gaps in weather information can be filled in with GEOS satellite data and advanced algorithms that can determine the most likely weather conditions between reporting stations. In doing so, weather could be shown in blocks of 5 km instead of the huge geographical sections traditional reports provide. Those 5 km blocks are updated every five minutes, allowing pilots to see up-to-date weather information for the entire flight area, instead of just at the selected airports.

It also allowed for weather to be shown at lower altitudes and in smaller increments. Instead of only having wind information at 3,000, 6,000 and 9,000 feet, we could now get that information at 1,000, 1,500, 2,000, etc. One of the most important changes was the decision to show weather at above ground level altitudes instead of mean sea level. This change reduces the probability of errors in determining the actual elevation of weather conditions above the surface, which is critical in combating controlled flight into terrain types of accidents, such as IIMC.

"The need for aircrews to have better weather resources both before and during flight is beyond dispute. International Helicopter Safety Team studies have found that a high percentage of accidents occur when returning to base or aircraft repositioning, not on the initial portion of a flight."

Furthermore, the team decided the information would be best utilized if it were in a visual format, instead of text-heavy. For example, colored layers were chosen to show weather conditions, and wind barbs are scattered around the map, painting an obvious picture that can be interpreted in seconds.

NCAR used one of its existing products, the Flight Path Tool, as the template for the new product. The Flight Path Tool is also worth a look. It can be found on the same website (www.aviationweather.gov), under the "tools" tab. What the administration came up with was an instant hit with the HAA community and others. According to the website, the HEMS Weather Tool is "specifically designed to show weather conditions for short-distance and low-altitude flights." The appeal to other industries is obvious, and law enforcement aviation was quick to put the new resource to work.

The experimental version of the tool was utilized by a daily average of 1,200 individual users. We can only guess at the number of lives this resource helped save during that time, but it is safe to say there were many. Seeing the value of the resource, FAA successfully brought the new product through the difficult process of gaining full government funding so it could be moved out of the experimental phase. As a result of the process, it was transferred to NOAA's Aviation Weather Center, where it currently resides.

The need for aircrews to have better weather resources both before and during flight is beyond dispute. International Helicopter Safety Team (IHST) studies have found that a high percentage of accidents occur when returning to base or aircraft repositioning, not on the initial portion of a flight. In fact, the only activity type that had more accidents was flight training.

That same IHST report listed pilot ground duties and situational awareness as the third and fourth most prevalent pilot-related contributing factors in accidents. Under the category of ground duties, improper or insufficient flight planning was at the top of the list. Loss of situational awareness related to weather and visibility was second in that category.

By choosing a visual format instead of relying on text, the HEMS weather tool offers an easy to read picture of a flight area at a glance. Different weather elements can also be depicted at the same time on the map, giving a more complete view of the entire situation at once. However, the creators and administrators still point out some limitations.

First, the current tool does not have a forecast option for ceilings, visibility or flight category. As mentioned, it is not usually the current weather that kills us; it is the weather that we encounter later, during the return to base or second leg of a flight. The current program managers are hoping to make resources available to the tool so weather probabilities one to two hours in the future can be displayed.

A second limitation is related to the non-traditional weather reporting sources. The availability of additional weather reports varies from place to place. The quality of the reports and applicability to aviation vary, as well. NOAA is hoping to add information from the Meteorlogical Assimilation Data Ingest System to boost the amount and quality of information fed into the tool. Additionally, many of the reporting sources do not meet the strict FAA standards needed to be considered reliable for planning a flight.

Because of this, the tool is intended to be used for a "no-go" call or return to base while in flight. It is not the official source required to make the "go" call. Carmichael relates it to the UNICOM or CTAF "line boy" weather briefing. When we are en route to an uncontrolled airport, we often call up the FBO on the radio ahead of time and inquire about the weather. While the FBO employees are not official weather briefers, when they tell you they cannot see past the first taxiway because of fog, the information is valuable and probably accurate. It would be prudent to use that report to determine if we should continue flying to that airport or start looking at the alternate.

We all need to look at numerous sources of weather information during our flight planning. This is true even for local flights at low flight levels. No matter how great the HEMS Weather Tool (or whatever weather product you love) is at depicting weather, we still need to look at the bigger picture to understand what is driving the weather we will be flying through at the local level. A surface analysis or "prog chart" is one required part of my personal daily weather briefing. Knowing where the weather systems are, what direction the fronts are moving and where the ridges are popping up helps explain the weather I am seeing on the HEMS tool. As mentioned, you still need to check weather forecasts, such as TAFs, for predictions on future weather changes.

There is a ton of weather information out there; most of it is free. A word of caution though is that most of it is made for the non-flying population. While much of the information looks impressive, remember those forecasts are produced for people who have no intention of flying through it. Know the difference between base radar and composite and what information you can get from each.

Are you interested in seeing where rain is hitting the ground or where turbulence associated with developing thunderstorms is forming? The local news weather forecast and most phone apps are for land-lovers who risk having their picnic rained out if the prediction is wrong. Those who produce aviation related weather information know that lives are at stake in the air, which influences the type of information and product quality they deliver.

Another factor to consider is the fact that even the best weather observations and forecasts cannot be 100 percent accurate 100 percent of the time. Expect that. Plan for it. Use en route decision points (EDPs). EDPs are set altitude and airspeed limits that tell the flight crew it is either time to go back home or land ASAP. To make EDPs work, we need to factor in a margin of error between what we have determined these limits to be and the reported or forecast weather. Say we set a minimum cloud ceiling of 1,000 feet above ground level for a hypothetical aviation unit. Anything below that has been determined to be unacceptably risky for the unit's operation. If the reported weather is 1,000 feet when we are dispatched, do we go? What if it is wrong and the clouds are actually at 800 feet? We turn around and come back, right?

Remember what the second highest category of flight activity was in the IHST study on accidents? Returning to base. If we are going to safely respond to deteriorating weather while in flight, either by returning to base, diverting or landing ASAP, we need a cushion between our minimum safe altitudes and the actual weather. Build it in.

I would like to commend NCAR, FAA, NEMSPA and NOAA for coming together to develop a fantastic weather resource for those of us otherwise forgotten souls. If you have not tried it, I highly recommend you do. If you use it, please click on the feedback link on the tool and let them know what you think. For those of you who live outside the U.S., take a look at the product and recommend something similar to your aviation governing authority if they have not already developed something.

Remember, it is not usually the weather at the airport when we start a flight that gets us. It is rarely the serious storms that can be seen miles away like the coming apocalypse that cause us to crash. It is the grey, broken, marginal weather that fades into danger before we realize, or at least accept, what is happening. Resources such as the HEMS Weather Tool are proving there are new ways to counter this threat.

A FRESH LOOK AT OLD TECHNOLOGY:
Why Error Management Checklists Keep Aircrews Safer

Like most pilots, I love having a new gadget in the aircraft, especially if it makes a significant impact on my ability to catch bad guys or complete my flight in a safer manner. Most of us use technology rather than develop it. However, we all use and are able to work on the development side of at least one piece of safety technology. It is a technology we often take for granted as a relic of the early days of aviation. However, what we consider to be common-sense has recently become a breakthrough safety improvement method in professions such as the medical field. What is this critical whiz-bang safety tool? The mighty checklist.

I know that ragged piece of paper with torn up lamination stuffed into some out-of-the-way pocket is not as exciting as a new glass panel display or magic bad guy finder. But it is one of the most important things keeping you safe during your flight operations, and some aspects of it that are not often considered may offer a way to improve its risk mitigation potency.

Many industries have taken the lead from aviation to improve safety and efficiency. The favor is often returned, as the interest from new fields can create fresh research and implementation perspectives we can use. James Reason, creator of the famous "Swiss Cheese" risk management model and one of the most popular researchers in the field, did a study on memory aids for the medical field. His research also applies to our favorite checklists.

According to Reason's research, "Combating Omission Errors Through Task Analysis and Good Reminders," checklists are used for two basic tasks. First, we use them to minimize errors (usually omissions). Second, they offer a chance to "contain" an error in procedures. This second characteristic is not as well recognized. However, both benefits are realized by using a before landing, or GUMPS (gas, undercarriage, mixture, prop, switches), checklist and a final approach check, for example. The GUMPS checklist ensures we initially perform all the required tasks. The additional checklist after turning final contains earlier omissions before they can cause a mishap.

This example may seem obvious, but consider where else in your operation you could use a similar error containment checklist. Perhaps a post-preflight checklist to ensure all cowlings, covers and doors have been secured following inspection? A quick check of the National Transportation Safety Board database shows such a checklist could have prevented numerous aviation accidents.

Another suggestion would be to have on-scene initial and follow-up checklists. Once over a mission location, a checklist could ensure the pilot/crew verifies nearby obstacles, emergency landing areas and engine instruments. The clock on the instrument panel could then be started and a follow up check could be conducted at a predetermined interval to make sure critical tasks have been completed, such as monitoring engine instruments or switching fuel tanks.

When we do everything correctly, these checks may seem unnecessary. But it is on those days when we are just a little off and have been circling a relatively mundane call that we could use a regular check to make sure we did not forget to perform, or maintain, a potentially important task. This critical double-check should be done as often as possible. After all, checklists are performed by humans, and while we can minimize human error, it is impossible to eliminate it.

Reason's research showed checklists were almost twice as effective as memorizing lists. Interestingly, he found using clocks or alarms was even more ineffective than memorization. What method do you use to check your fuel level? What is the backup check if you let the primary reminder slip? What about other critical tasks?

Several simple tricks can minimize error and speed up the checklist process. First is the order of tasks within the list. Often, an order is dictated to us, but in some cases, we have a choice. One of my mentors, Richard Bray, Chief Pilot of the Alachua County (FL) Sheriff's Office, explained during my training that a good checklist has an orderly flow through the cockpit. Instead of jumping around from an overhead panel to the top right side of the instrument panel, down to the center console and back to another random location, the checklists he made for his air-craft started at one point and flowed through a specific panel before moving on to the next section (with a few unavoidable exceptions).

Orderly checklists help us avoid inadvertently skipping items, especially in a profession where people are often screaming for us to get in the air as soon as possible. If we accidently miss an item while going through the list, our eyes will catch it as they sweep across the pattern. I can recall a number of times my finger was tracing the pattern across the instrument panel as we conducted a checklist and I suddenly stopped at an item I realized had been inadvertently skipped.

This is also useful in checklists traditionally done from memory, such as emergency procedures. The age-old "inverted U" response to an engine failure was taught to me two decades ago in a single-engine Cessna. Moving from the fuel selector valve on the floor and up and around to the master switch has helped me ensure I hit all the important parts of the checklist, even during stressful examinations.

How could someone skip a checklist item? We are often in a rush to launch on a call, sometimes in the middle of the night, looking at a black and white, 8-point font under dim cockpit lighting. It happens. Even using the highly recommended call-and-response method of having one crewmember read the checklist to the other is not fool-proof. An error management technique is to provide a means of helping the user maintain their place in the checklist. Alternating the color of each row works well and allows you to mark critical tasks. (Make sure the colors remain visible under your preferred color of night lighting.) Reason's research showed that numbered lists produced fewer omissions than those without numbers.

The items at the bottom of a checklist are generally more prone to omission. As we get close to the end of a list, we tend to increase our pace through the tasks in an effort to complete the series and move on. This is especially dangerous in our profession, where we find ourselves under pressure to perform tasks quickly so we can move on with our mission. A fantastic tip that was given to me by an APSA member is to increase the font size on the last few items on the list.

This stumbling block is compounded if the checklist continues past a major objective—the tasks past that point are more likely to be skipped. According to Reason, the user's mind may subconsciously finish the checklist once the main result of the series is achieved and disregard the rest. For example, if the engine start checklist has items beyond the point where the engine is started and stabilized, they are prone to omission. Move those items to the next checklist, in this case a pre-taxi, post-start or other similar list.

Checklist items are more likely to be completed if the operator fully understands the reason for the item. Is that required time before shutdown really a "cool down," or is it is required for another reason? Is that avionics step really "setting" the indicator or "testing" it? When checking the hydraulics, what exactly are you looking for and what warrants a no-go during the ops check? Training officers may find some shocking answers to questions like these if their pilots and/or TFOs have been going through the steps without really understanding them. This is a great item to include in regular currency training.

According to Reason, one of the biggest barriers to the safety benefits checklists provide us is the idea that a professional simply should not make errors in the first place. The belief that checklists are for new guys or that using a checklist is a sign that someone is not a good enough pilot to perform tasks from memory too often keeps this life-saving tool tucked away. Our limited view of this powerful system also robs the TFO of a potentially useful tool. TFO checklists can ensure the officers are set up prior to flight or arriving at a scene. Finally, we tend to justify skipping checklists by saying we are in a hurry to a hot call and don't have time because lives are at stake.

By taking a new look at the checklist, we can make a few simple upgrades to this age-old piece of aviation technology. Reorder the items into a flow through the cockpit, add color, numbers or varying fonts to help the operator keep track of his or her place, make sure your crews fully understand each item, and engineer in secondary checks to contain errors when completing initial and reoccurring tasks. And for you die-hard tech buffs—ditch the laminator and put your checklists on a tablet computer.

Upgraded checklists will not only make your operation safer, but they will also allow the crew to get through the items faster and more consistently, reducing response times and increasing success rates.

ENROUTE DECISION POINTS:
Response to Deteriorating Conditions

I started flying as a teenager at an out-of-the-way grass airfield populated solely by gliders and fabric covered tail-draggers. The "office" was a section of a barn decorated with hundreds of pieces of aviation memorabilia, a bar and a variety of chairs for pilots to sit in and share tales of questionable factual accuracy. There was no computer, and I don't remember anyone ever calling for a weather briefing. We had a "weather window." If the weather window did not indicate "blue" or possibly "blue and slightly white," we would remain in the chairs and get another soft drink from behind the bar. The windsock was visible as well. We were flying for fun, and the window worked just fine.

In public safety aviation, our weather window is composed of computer-based weather charts and reports in addition to the commonsense method of simply looking outside. Sometimes what we see when we look at the weather makes go/no-go decisions easy. But often, the answer is not so obvious. Let's face it—no matter how much we enjoy our jobs, we are not flying for fun. We are flying to protect our community, and sometimes our community needs us most when the weather is not ideal. It is these scenarios that lead to far too many funerals for our peers.

Many weather-related accidents start out in conditions that are okay at launch but deteriorate during flight. A report from the International Helicopter Safety Team found that the second most common activity being conducted when accidents occur is returning to base or repositioning.

We all know weather forecasts are not 100 percent reliable. Unfortunately, forecasts for poor or changing weather are far less accurate than a forecast for good weather. Some estimates give forecasts for changing conditions an accuracy of only 45 percent compared to 75 percent for good weather. Changing ceiling and visibility forecasts beyond two to three hours should be considered low probability estimates. One study from the Massachusetts Institute of Technology found forecasts for ceiling and visibility averaged about 70 percent accurate at the one-hour mark but fell to 50 percent after three to four hours. Fast moving cold fronts are typically easier to forecast than slow moving warm fronts.

Let's assume the weather is marginal for an operation. The conditions are not great, but our policy and personal minimums still allow the flight. We want to answer the request for service, and we feel the aircraft and crew are equipped and trained to safely conduct the flight in the current conditions. Still, we recognize that the conditions could change during the flight. How can we reduce these risks in a reasonable manner?

First, dial a protective barrier into your weather limits. If your unit (or personal) limit has determined 1,000 feet, 3 miles and 30 knots are the limits of acceptable risk, give yourself an opportunity to return to base safely under those conditions. What the limits are will depend on your aircraft, unit training, terrain, average distance from landing areas, local weather, etc. In our example here, let's make the takeoff minimum 1,200 feet, 4 miles and 25 knots. What we have done is given ourselves a layer of protection from deteriorating weather conditions and the opportunity to get the aircraft to the nearest landing area under what we have determined to be acceptable weather conditions.

The second defense against the marginal weather trap is an enroute decision point (EDP). EDPs have been developed and promoted by aeromedical community members in response to the unacceptably high number of weather related accidents in the industry. An EDP procedure is considered to be part of a three-component system. The first two components are a safety culture and flight risk assessment tool.

The culture of the unit must promote and support aircrews making the right decision when it comes to weather.

When I was a new pilot, my chief pilot Richard Bray had about 10 times the flight time and 100 times the experience I did. Still, when I made a weather related no-go decision, he backed me 100 percent. Had he taken flights after I said I couldn't go, it would have negatively influenced my future decisions and the culture of the unit.

The flight risk assessment tool is something I have spoken about quite a bit in the past, so let's move on to the third component, the actual EDP.

"Sometimes what we see when we look at the weather makes go/no-go decisions easy. But often, the answer is not so obvious. Let's face it—no matter how much we enjoy our jobs, we are not flying for fun. We are flying to protect our community, and sometimes our community needs us most when the weather is not ideal."

One of my favorite quotes is from U.S. Navy Admiral Chester Nimitz: "Ships that keep on going as long as the severity of wind and sea has not yet come close to capsizing them or breaking them in two may nevertheless become helpless to avoid these catastrophes later if things get worse. The time for taking all measures for a ship's safety is while still able to do so."

The EDP is a set of criteria that will prompt the flight crew to make a decision and respond to deteriorating conditions before they become a serious problem. The decision point is defined by a certain altitude and/or airspeed reduction. The aeromedical industry recommends using a reduction of 30 knots below cruise or descent to 500 feet above ground level for transport flights.

Many of us perform medical flights, and these recommendations may work well for those agencies. However, our industry also includes a variety of other public safety missions that may require different criteria.

I typically fly patrol flights, and we are rarely "enroute" anywhere, other than to the next orbit or random call location. We also fly at patrol airspeed, not cruise, and a 30-knot reduction would often put us near effective translational lift. For our operation, a set of two decision altitudes works best. One altitude should trigger a return to base. The second, lower altitude would prompt the crew to abandon the plan to return to base and instead find a nearby landing zone. If you fly over flat terrain, mean sea level altitudes work fine. If you fly in mountainous or varying terrain, you may want to use AGL altitudes.

Depending on your operation, you may have a third option, which is to transfer to IFR flight. The intention is to set up and go IFR before entering instrument conditions if your aircraft and crew are instrument certified, current and proficient. If any of these four conditions cannot be met (certified, current, proficient and not yet in IMC), this option will not work as advertised. Whatever your choice is, you must do something other than continue VFR into the deteriorating conditions.

How does this work in the real world? Let's say a flight crew completed a FRAT and sees the weather is flyable but marginal. The crew sets the EDP and decides, "Okay, we're going to go fly, but if we have to descend to X feet, we're coming home, and if we have to descend to Y feet, we're landing at the first suitable LZ instead of returning to base." The crew could set limits on airspeed, if appropriate.

All aircrew members must be in agreement and understand the EDP. During the flight, the TFO might look at the altimeter and say, "Hey, are we at X feet?" The pilot should respond that he has been descending to stay under the ceiling, and they are now at X feet. The TFO responds by hanging up the camera controller and saying, "Let's go home."

It seems simple, because it is. However, if done properly, an EDP can be as powerful as it is simple. Some may ask, "Why do it?" With all the variabilities in weather and human factors at play and the sheer number of talented and skilled peers killed in these conditions, why not try it?

IIMC TRAINING & AWARENESS IS CRUCIAL PART OF SAFETY

Do you know inadvertent entry into instrument meteorological conditions is dangerous? Do you know you should train for it? If I ask these two questions to any group of public safety aviators, the answer is almost always a resounding yes. If you are new to the industry, the answer is yes for good reason. The combination of weather and/or darkness that eliminates the ability to fly by reference to external visual cues (i.e. the horizon) and the absence of planning or preparation for flight in those conditions is extremely lethal. The question that gets trickier to answer is, "How should we train for IIMC?"

If we look at some of the IIMC accidents in our industry and others, we find a large number of them occur in aircraft equipped for instrument flight with instrument rated pilots. The AOPA Nall Report found that an instrument rated pilot was involved in 46 percent of all weather-related accidents. And an FAA study on pilot performance in IIMC found that "analysis of the effect of total pilot time...was not found to be significant for most measures. The few statistically significant effects of pilot time in fact showed increasing errors with pilot time, not decreasing as one might expect."

How can an experienced pilot trained to fly in instrument conditions crash simply because they fly into the exact weather they have been trained to fly in? Is it because the aircraft is not instrument certified? Unfortunately, we have suffered IIMC accidents in both instrument certified and instrument-capable helicopters and fixed-wing aircraft.

We train for IMC very well. The problem is the "inadvertent" part of IIMC. Consider the differences between planned and unplanned IMC operations, as outlined by the APSA workgroup.

In planned IMC flight:
- IMC conditions are expected, making it a low-key event.
- Aircrews have time to prepare equipment, brief the flight, refresh skills, setup the cockpit.
- The aircraft usually enters IMC in a level climb, on course.
- The flight is already in the IFR system with air traffic control.
- Pilots have conditioned exclusion of VFR flight techniques.
- Crews are working to maintain situational awareness.

In unplanned (inadvertent) IMC flight:
- Neither the equipment nor cockpit is set up, and no IFR briefing has occurred.
- The pilot is caught off guard and not ready or expecting IMC, causing stress and sometimes panic.
- The aircraft is often not in level flight or on course.
- The flight is usually not active in the IFR system with air traffic control.
- The pilot is tempted to continue to utilize VFR flying techniques.
- Denial causes a delay in response (most spatial disorientation accidents occur within two minutes of onset).
- The crew is working to recover situational awareness.

Instrument training usually focuses on planned IMC factors. Often, what we consider IIMC training looks a lot like regular IMC training with several unusual attitude recoveries preceding an instrument approach.

Consider a hypothetical training mission in which the pilot and CFI brief the entire flight, including approach frequencies, flight path and instrument approaches to be conducted. All charts and approach plates are marked, printed off or brought up on a tablet for immediate reference in the cockpit, even if they are not normally carried in that manner.

After aircraft startup, the pilot puts in all frequencies that will be needed, sets up the avionics for the route and approach and perhaps even gets an instrument clearance from ATC.

The pilot is talking to ATC during climb-out to a specific altitude, often well above regular operational altitude, and is on a set course determined by ATC or the CFI.

After takeoff, the CFI takes the controls and tells the pilot to put on a view limiting device (foggles). The pilot takes his/her time putting them on, making sure they can see as much as possible out of the bottom without being obvious, including the chin bubble on helicopters. The CFI then returns control of the aircraft back to the pilot in straight and level flight, perhaps still in a stable climb.

After a few minutes of instrument flight to get used to flying instruments again, the CFI takes the controls and puts the aircraft through several Top Gun style turns while having the pilot close their eyes to achieve "unusual attitudes." The pilot then flies the instrument approaches, as was briefed before the flight. Does any of this address the specific issues listed above for unplanned instrument flight? No.

Planned instrument flight training is important. It teaches the skills needed to control an aircraft and operate in the air traffic control system without reference to visual cues outside the aircraft. However, after these skills are obtained, we need to add specific unplanned IMC flight training based on the elements listed above. The best way to do this is with a realistic scenario based on operation type.

Now imagine a patrol operation in which the CFI and pilot go up for a quarterly training flight covering a number of maneuvers. To manage risk and maximize learning, all maneuvers are briefed, including IIMC.

However, this time, only the IIMC procedures are included in the briefing, not the specifics of the scenario. The cockpit is set up as it normally is for a patrol flight. Only charts and approach plates normally carried by the pilot are available. Radios are set up as usual. The flight is conducted at night to limit visual cues available to the pilot during the IIMC portion of the flight. This closely simulates routine patrol operations.

During the flight, the CFI suggests you work through some patrol scenario and picks a series of targets for the pilot to orbit. During one of the orbits, the CFI reaches over and turns off the pilot's night vision goggles (NVGs). The

CFI instructs the pilot to leave the goggles down and recover using the IIMC procedure. The pilot stabilizes the aircraft and starts down the checklist. After simulating ATC contact and declaring an emergency, the pilot first attempts to get vectors to VFR conditions. After learning VFR conditions are not within range of the aircraft, an instrument approach is conducted.

In this hypothetical scenario, we have utilized instrument flying skills but in a framework that is closer to a realistic IIMC situation. If you do not fly with NVGs or wish to do this during the day, there are view-limiting devices that flip up and down on hinges near the arms of foggles. Using these, you can reach over at any time and flip down the visor.

If a unit decides to perform this type of training, a word of caution is appropriate for CFIs. Stay close on the controls, even with experienced pilots. We are simulating an emergency. It is an emergency where people die because of spatial disorientation. As with any simulated emergency, there is a possibility of the pilot receiving instruction to do the wrong thing.

Do you regularly fly with other crewmembers, such as a tactical flight officer? Why not include them in your IIMC scenario? Remember that some of the unique factors in an unplanned IMC are the facts that the cockpit and avionics are not set up and charts are not immediately available. A TFO or other crewmember can easily do these things for the pilot, if you train both crewmembers to respond to IIMC this way. The CFI in the above scenario can perform some tasks the unit's TFOs are trained to do. However, having TFOs trained to perform these tasks is critical.

Another major factor in IIMC is that the pilot is working to regain situational awareness instead of simply maintaining it. The TFO or other crewmember can assist here as well. What kills people in IIMC events is not the weather itself but loss of control of the aircraft that leads to controlled flight into terrain (CFIT). If you've had instrument training, you probably remember the instructor saying things like, "Watch your bank" or "Check your airspeed." The comments are enough to help you recognize a lapse in situational awareness and initiate corrective action.

Training a TFO to call out deviations in bank, pitch, airspeed and altitude can have the same effect. Again, this requires training the TFO on when to call out deviations and training the pilot to accept the help. Even a TFO in the back seat of an aircraft can pull up flight instruments on various types of avionics, mission equipment or a tablet and help out—if trained.

To prevent an unfavorable outcome (e.g. CFIT), we can react to the unsafe event that can lead to it (e.g. IIMC) or prevent the event from occurring. Our IIMC recovery training to this point has only addressed the reaction to the event. We should include prevention in our training scenarios. The use of a flight risk assessment tool (FRAT) is a good place to start. FRATs should be completed as a crew, not just by the pilot. For the TFO or other crewmember to be an effective part of the FRAT process, they need to be trained to do it.

Another preventative measure to train for is an enroute decision point (EDP). An EDP involves choosing an altitude and airspeed that will trigger a decision. That decision may be to turn around and return to base or land the aircraft. You may choose two EDPs to cover the decision to turn back and then to land. During your scenario, brief these EDPs. While in flight, simulate deteriorating weather conditions. Continue to simulate lowering conditions until the pilot makes the appropriate decision or the TFO speaks up and asks for the pilot/CFI to respond appropriately.

Don't have a second crewmember to count on? Do you have dispatchers or ground personnel you can train to help prevent IIMC? How about preloading the avionics, radios and charts needed to properly respond to unplanned IMC flight on every operational flight, or at least when weather is marginal? Whatever you choose, train for it.

Reliable performance of a task in an emergency situation requires actually doing the task in training. Talking about it simply is not effective. It may feel silly to some calling out the EDP or aircraft attitude deviations during training flights, but it must be done. CFIs will find themselves asking, "what would you do at this point?" and hearing responses such as, "Oh, well if this were a real scenario, I would have said [the correct answer], but [insert excuse of choice here]." The CFI's response should be, "Good, I want to hear you say it. Let's do it again."

If you get a chance to fly in a simulator, ask the instructor to set the weather conditions to a quarter-mile visibility. You will notice it is not too difficult to fly at this setting and that a bit of the ground is still visible at the bottom of the screen. This is especially true for helicopter pilots who can see out of the chin bubble. You will also notice it is familiar, because this visibility setting is close to what we can achieve with traditional view limiting devices (foggles).

Ask the simulator instructor to lower conditions from a quarter-mile to zero visibility and you may find your workload increasing dramatically. The FAA study on helicopter pilot performance in IIMC mentioned above also found pilot loss of control increased dramatically below a quarter-mile visibility. Instrument training in our aircraft usually is limited to a quarter-mile visibility, especially in helicopters that cannot legally enter IMC, so we fail to simulate the most critical conditions.

Everyone should experience flying in actual instrument conditions. However, even in instrument certified aircraft, it is difficult to combine IFR flight, which requires ATC coordination, and IIMC scenarios. A flight simulator, however, can simulate IIMC in zero visibility conditions. All the same rules apply, though—we do not want to mistake planned IMC training for unplanned. I once had a simulator instructor say, "Okay, we're going to do some IIMC now." The comment instantly removed any inadvertent element of the training.

All of the recommendations discussed here are included in APSA's updated IIMC Training Recommendations on the APSA website. Additionally, a free IIMC video and downloadable PowerPoint presentation are available.

The industry has been hitting this threat hard, with promising results. With continued training and awareness, we can deny an old enemy any new victims.

SAFETY TIPS TO AVOID, SURVIVE AND TRAIN FOR IIMC

I am writing these words only after knocking on wood and throwing salt over my shoulder. In 2019, our industry had gone four years without a fatal accident related to inadvertent flight into instrument meteorological conditions (IIMC). While loss of control incidents other than IIMC and those related to hoist operations have taken over as the most lethal accident categories in our industry, it is important to remember the many lessons we have learned over the years about IIMC.

In April 2013, APSA published IIMC training recommendations. At the time, IIMC had been the leading cause of fatalities in public safety aviation for decades. A group of individuals worked on identifying the gaps in industry operations and training and suggested several fundamental changes to the way we address the problem.

Following are a few highlights of the training recommendations, all of which are available on the safety page of the APSA website.

Avoidance Before Flight. Using a flight risk assessment tool to enhance crew resource management before a mission is a powerful way to stop IIMC before leaving the ground.

IIMC survival is about more than just accurate weather prediction. The aircrew's ability to avoid or respond to IIMC is dependent on human factors issues, such as fatigue, medication and proficiency.

Once an aircrew works together to identify the risk factors in an upcoming flight or shift, the team can mitigate them. This may involve gathering further weather information, reviewing an IIMC procedure or setting an enroute decision point (EDP). An EDP is a combination of altitudes and airspeeds the aircrew decides will trigger a return to base, divert to an alternate location or land at the nearest suitable landing zone or airport.

Avoidance During Flight. Once the crewmembers are properly briefed on a flight, they must stick to the plan. When an EDP has been set and alternate landing areas identified, the hard part is actually diverting or landing when the point is reached. It is easy to make excuses and justify another five minutes or another hundred feet. This is why setting trigger points, such as EDPs, during flight is generally ineffective.

Train your aircrew members to identify decision points and insist pilots divert or land as appropriate. If we don't hold each other to these decisions in the aircraft, no one will.

Bosses must empower their aircrews to make the right call to protect agency aircraft and personnel when faced with not only IIMC, but also any threat to the safe conclusion of a flight. Encourage precautionary landings and spell the procedures out in your policy manual.

If you are approaching IMC conditions in an IFR-certified aircraft and properly rated and proficient, that is the time to obtain in-flight clearance and enter the soup on your terms.

Surviving IIMC. If we have failed to avoid IIMC, a few tips can help us survive. First, IIMC is a loss of control accident that ends in controlled flight into terrain. Maintaining aircraft control, not diving away from the clouds, is the priority.

Most IIMC accidents occur during a turn. All crewmembers should concentrate on keeping the aircraft straight and level for at least the first two minutes. An exception to this would be a turn needed to avoid hitting rising terrain or obstacles. If any change is made to the flight attitude, it should be a climb away from the ground, unless a climb will bring you into icing conditions.

A TFO or other aircrew can concentrate on watching the attitude indicator, airspeed and altitude, calling out any deviations the same way an instrument flight instructor would. Watch the yaw—it's easy to forget. Engage an autopilot if you have one onboard and have trained for its application in IIMC. An autopilot can make things worse if you are not proficient. Maintain control of the aircraft and regain situational awareness.

Once you have regained control over the situation, it's time to navigate. Have the TFO or other aircrew member, if available, dial in air traffic control and declare an emergency. ATC wants you to declare an emergency so their hands are untied and they are free to help you. Even if your aircraft is IFR-certified, IIMC is an emergency. The U.S. Coast Guard lost an HH-65 and the U.S. Army an H-60 in the Gulf of Mexico within the last few years after IIMC encounters. Both aircraft were IFR-certified, with IFR-rated pilots at the controls. Until recently, the leading cause of fatalities for law enforcement fixed-wing crews was IIMC.

"All crewmembers should concentrate on keeping the aircraft straight and level for at least the first two minutes of IIMC. An exception would be a turn needed to avoid hitting rising terrain or obstacles. If any change is made to the flight attitude, it should be a climb away from the ground, unless a climb will bring you into icing conditions."

After declaring an emergency, tell ATC what you want to do next. If you are IFR-certified and proficient, continue on IFR. If you are not, look for VFR conditions. Hopefully, an airport or landing zone is nearby and ATC can vector you to it for a visual approach. If not, it's time to pick the instrument approach with which you're most comfortable. Having a trained TFO or other aircrew member dial in the approach and any related avionics and find the approach plate to brief you is invaluable.

Additional aircrew members must stay vigilant, watching the attitude instruments throughout the IIMC process. Many pilots cannot help but look at the avionics, even when someone else is taking care of the tasks properly. In IMC, under stress, the controls tend to follow the eyes and an innocent look at the GPS can induce an unnoticed 30-degree roll within seconds.

Training for IIMC. IIMC training must be fundamentally different than training for planned IMC. Don't forget about the "inadvertent" part. When doing IIMC training, give no notice. The cockpit should not be pre-loaded for IMC with charts, frequencies and approaches, unless that is the way you always fly. The focus should be on aircraft control and regaining it after a loss of situational awareness or unusual attitude.

The scenario should be based on a normal operational mission, not a planned IFR flight, unless that is your normal mission. Training must include all aircrew members. Non-pilot TFOs and other aircrew can be trained to handle the tasks in the cockpit except for operating the flight controls. The most critical thing they can do is call out attitude deviations, especially for the first two minutes after entering IMC. Many will be hesitant to say anything.

If you are using a simulator, conduct the entire flight under marginal weather conditions and encompass IIMC in a session that covers numerous emergency procedures. If the weather is marginal, you can throw the aircraft into IMC quickly, instead of changing a blue sky to a 500-foot ceiling. This allows for an element of surprise when initiating the IIMC scenario.

IIMC continues to claim the lives of aviation industry members on a regular basis. Despite our industry sector's lack of recent accidents, we cannot allow ourselves to be lulled into a false sense of security. The operational risks that make IIMC a threat have not diminished. We must continue to put effort into maintaining our IIMC avoidance and survival programs.

WORKING TOGETHER:
Deploying Manned and Unmanned
Aircraft Safely & Successfully

I love catching bad guys from the air. Absolutely love it. And finding and rescuing lost people, especially children and those in critical need, will be some of the defining moments of my life. Above all, when I meet each public safety officer I serve, a voice in my head reminds me, "This person is counting on you." This is what motivates me to incorporate any tool I can acquire to do my job as effectively as possible—including unmanned aircraft systems.

Imagine a critical incident in your area of responsibility. An active shooter is moving in and out of buildings in a business complex, taking shots from random windows. Your manned aircraft is overhead coordinating the perimeter set by ground units, calling out victim locations around the facility, and simultaneously looking for the shooter to exit a door or open a window to take a shot. Rifle teams want information about where to make entry, combined police and EMS groups are trying to access victims you are calling out, the supervisor asks if the perimeter has holes, someone says they saw the shooter on the south roof and seconds later more shots come from the east entrance windows, suggesting multiple shooters.

The situation may seem extreme, but it is not outside the realm of possibility for many public safety aviators. What if we could add one or even two small UAS assets to the scenario? What if we had the ability to coordinate tasking, splitting the airborne support responsibilities between manned and unmanned crews so one could watch the perimeter while another searches below treetop level in the courtyards and windows and a third went in ahead of the entry team?

Obviously, we need to do some training, establish procedures and develop tactics before we consistently operate manned and unmanned aircraft on the same missions. But with a few things in mind, we can accomplish the goal while staying safe throughout the flights.

To address manned and unmanned aircraft separation, we need two layers of safety, as no risk control is 100 percent effective. The first layer is altitude separation, which is relatively easy for units operating manned aircraft with camera systems or binoculars, because the optimum altitude for effective use is 1,000 feet AGL or higher. UAS operations are typically limited by regulations or camera capability to 400 feet AGL.

Several operators I have engaged via APSA's online UAS and safety monthly meetings said their programs require a minimum of 500 feet between aircraft. If your manned aircraft must fly lower than 900 feet or your unmanned asset must be above 400 feet, a different solution is required. In any case, a layer of vertical separation protects against loss of aircraft control, accidental altitude deviation, etc. If a pilot loses situational awareness or control of the aircraft, a 500-foot cushion can disappear quickly.

In addition to vertical separation, lateral manned and unmanned aircraft separation provides a second layer of protection. We can achieve lateral separation by making lines on a map and keeping the aircraft in different sectors. For example, we could select a roadway and say one aircraft must be on the east side, while the other remains on the west side. With a larger search area, we could assign grids or other defined land sections to individual aircraft.

What if our manned and unmanned aircraft must view the same location? In this scenario, we can assign distances from a point of interest. For example, aircraft A could be allowed from the point of interest to 0.2 miles out, aircraft B could be assigned from 0.2 to 0.4 miles out, and aircraft C could be given 0.4 miles out and beyond.

Or we could assign aircraft A to fly directly over the point of interest, for example a mall, aircraft B could patrol from the edge of the mall to the edge of the parking lot, and aircraft C could operate outside the parking lot. We could then assign altitude blocks to each section. In the end, the plan would look like a mini class B airspace around the call location.

When determining the geographic sections for each aircraft, we must consider capabilities and how the search needs to be conducted in each sector. If the UAS is operated line-of-sight, the ground crew will require access to a location near the aircraft's assigned sector.

Each aircraft must also identify at least one emergency landing area. For UAS, this will often be the operators' location. We should also look for a location under the assigned area to steer the aircraft in the event of a malfunction, lost communications, unexpected weather, etc. Once the locations are identified, a simple abort or emergency call over the radio can direct all aircraft to the preplanned landing zones without further communication.

UAS are difficult to see from an aircraft, even when aircrews know where to look. Manned aircraft are much easier for ground operators to see. If a manned crew loses visual contact with an unmanned aircraft, the UAS operator must clearly explain where the vehicle is in relation to the manned aircraft. A flashing beacon, even during the day, is worth considering.

Once we have separated our aircraft, we must establish communications. Two conversations need to be facilitated simultaneously, before and while the aircraft work together in the air. First, we discuss the call itself. We need information from other ground units and dispatchers about the mission and a means of relaying information about what we find during our search.

The pilots of each aircraft must have direct and unimpeded lines of communication. They must establish, verify and maintain the aircraft separation plan. If any kind of in-flight emergency or abnormality occurs, the pilots must immediately communicate it. A radio channel already full of mission-related chatter may not allow the pilots to immediately talk to one another in situations when seconds matter.

The method of communication will depend on the radio capabilities of the UAS, manned aircraft and ground teams. Some operators use aviation band radios for pilots, while others select a second band on the public safety radios due to encryption concerns. Whatever you choose, two different radio channels will likely be needed to facilitate the two communication requirements for combined manned and unmanned operations.

Planning for combined operations doesn't stop with aircraft separation and communications. As with any operation, we must train for both normal and abnormal operational tasks.

The normal tactics used to perform your mission will vary depending on your equipment and operational goals. Abnormal operations are more universal. For manned aircraft, mechanical failure or loss of control can occur. This could mean having to depart the area, or it could mean the aircraft is required to make an emergency landing in 20 seconds. The UAS team members should not be left to wonder where the aircraft is going or what to do. They must know how to move their aircraft out of the way and return to the ground. Does the UAS team know the difference between "emergency" and "precautionary" landings? Such conversations should occur before the mission, during training.

Does the manned aircraft crew understand the situation if the UAS team calls out a lost link, flyaway or loss of power? Which situations are controllable, and which are not? If there is an automatic return to the takeoff location, to what is the return-to-base altitude set? Can the UAS pilot use partial control to fly the aircraft into a tree or other object instead of a crowd or aircraft overhead? Can a teammate call out the emergency to the manned aircraft while the operator concentrates on flying? All considerations must be planned for and regarded as eventualities.

Operating unmanned aircraft along with manned aircraft creates too much work for one person to fly the UAS, operate the camera systems, maintain aircraft separation, and have both tactical and air safety conversations at the same time.

Can manned and unmanned aircraft operate simultaneously? They already have. Operational tips have come from the experiences of agencies deploying both aircraft successfully. The aircraft have worked together to divide mission tasking, relieve each other for refueling or battery changes and deploy their unique equipment and perspectives. Many of the agencies have the benefit of operating both manned and unmanned aircraft, allowing them to streamline training, policies and tactics into some of the most impressive examples of airborne public safety operations ever seen.

In the end, we must channel our love for protecting our sisters and brothers on the ground as fuel to drive innovation, training and professionalism. If we can find ways to operate more efficiently, we are obligated to do so.

CHAPTER 4

SAFETY
LESSONS

THE UNKNOWN RISK:
Lessons From A Red Bull Stunt Pilot

When I was hired by an agency that conducts hoisting operations, I didn't have much experience before starting their training. I would be a lousy safety guy if I pretended to be an expert on hoisting safety. This is a situation in which many of you find yourselves. Agencies are acquiring more capable aircraft at an increasing rate, and society is expecting more mission capabilities from us, such as hoisting, fire suppression and tactical support (fast roping, use of force, etc.). How do we maintain safety when venturing into the unknown?

I sought out some advice from someone who has experience in taking on the safety challenges of new frontiers. In 2015, Chuck Aaron was in his 10th year of flying aerobatic performances in the Red Bull helicopter. He was the only pilot licensed by the Federal Aviation Administration to perform aerobatics in a helicopter. Prior to his career as a professional pilot and licensed A&P mechanic, Aaron was a deputy sheriff in Orange County, FL. To say he understands managing risk would be a gross understatement.

Aaron has worked hard to disprove a common misconception about our industry. People tend to think we are cowboys (and girls) who take on risks with reckless bravado and little thought about consequences. Hollywood has driven that point home for decades.

Aaron told me he approached the aerobatics project with a methodical process. The first step was to assemble a group of people who could help him think through all the possible hazards and solutions. "We had camps," he said, including mechanics, test pilots and engineers. Part of this process was thinking through "an exit idea for each maneuver, planning how can I get out if it is not going right."

Only after this formal hazard identification and analysis did Aaron begin the "crawl-walk-run" process of practicing helicopter aerobatics. "I only attempted the maneuvers when conditions were perfect," he said. "And I stayed within my personal limits. If I am uncomfortable, I won't do it."

Take, for example, perfecting the loop. Aaron said the process was more about practicing exit strategies than the actual complete maneuver. "I worked on it more than 50 times, going 1 degree more each time," he said.

After each flight, the impact on the airframe was monitored by checking over the aircraft and reviewing the onboard recording instruments. By the time Aaron completed his first loop, he had become comfortable with the maneuver because he was proficient at performing it correctly and getting out of it if needed.

The process allowed Aaron to identify hazards as they began to reveal themselves, long before they posed serious risk. By evaluating each flight, he was able to identify problems with center of gravity, rotor RPM, aircraft stresses and flight control issues and mitigate them before they grew teeth big enough to bite.

This method is different from how we sometimes train. I have seen (and been guilty of) "just trying it out" or having a student do a complete maneuver, knowing it will be done poorly, with the intention of seeing what needs to be worked on. When we do that, we leap into the unknown, using only luck and assumption to mitigate risk. Aaron mitigates risk in uncharted territory because he doesn't jump blindly into it: "We can deal with the 'known'," he said, "so make it that way."

If we find ourselves flying beyond our comfort level, relying on educated guesses or depending on flawless execution because there is no room for error or opportunity to exit, it's likely we have not taken the time to prepare and train correctly.

Even with a methodical process such as this, we will not remove all risk. The goal is to lower risk as low as reasonably practical (ALARP). But what is that limit? At what point do we decide risk is as low as it will go, and who decides what remaining risk is acceptable? When making such decisions, Aaron said he asks himself, "Do I need to do this to accomplish my goal?" His aircraft is approved to pull up to 3.5 positive Gs and up to 1 negative G. "I never go close to those limits anymore," he said, adding that one shouldn't do something simply because they can, but because the mission requires it. Aaron says he learned to lower the G forces in his performances to 0-2.7 Gs. "I don't do negative Gs because I can get the job done without it," he said.

In other words, the increased risk involved in going right up to his certified limits is not worth any potential gain in his performance.

Another example is the forward flip. After evaluating the maneuver's wear on the airframe, Aaron realized the risk could not be lowered to an acceptable level, so he chose not to do it. He was authorized to do the maneuver, and no one would have questioned him if he'd decided to include it in his routine. He made an educated and informed decision that the risk outweighed the benefit. This is a powerful lesson for us all from a guy who does some of the most incredible flying ever done in helicopter. How do we decide what ALARP is? We examine what we need to do to get the job done and what we have trained for, not what we are legally allowed to do.

This isn't the end of the story. Just as safety management systems require performance assessments of risk controls, Aaron continues to assure his safety precautions are working. He uses onboard instrumentation and cameras to conduct post flight evaluations of his performance and the impact on the aircraft. After 10 years of performing, he still looked for any breaks in the safety armor he's put in place and makes adjustments as needed. Doing something for a long time without an accident doesn't mean there is not room for improvement, especially where safety is concerned.

I asked Aaron how could we mitigate risk when dealing with the unknown. "Remove the unknown part of the equation," he said. "That's now NASA did it in the Apollo program. If you use a methodical process and go one step at a time, it can take you to the moon."

Aviation is an industry rooted in taking on new frontiers. Since the Wright Brothers, we have made it a pillar of our profession to do what everybody thinks is impossible. Every time society says something can't be done, a pilot soon comes along and does it. The list is long: manned flight, crossing the oceans, breaking the sound barrier, going to the moon, living in space, doing aerobatics in a helicopter. It's no wonder aviation has held a place of mystique and awe in modern society.

That powerful image of disregard for the impossible also gives aviators an undeserved reputation for being careless risk-takers. While sometimes true, this is usually not the case, especially for the best examples of professionals in the air.

Aaron has done what many considered impossible. He has done it safely and methodically in a manner that is anything but reckless. His mission has always been to inspire people, especially the youth, and get them excited about aviation, a mission in which he has been wildly successful. He is also an inspiration to those of us already in aviation. If he can do what he does safely, we can do what we do safely, if we choose to follow the same path of thoughtful, methodical risk mitigation and training. And for that, I would like to thank him.

EXTREME SAFETY: Tips to Manage Risk

- Remove the "unknown" part of the equation.

- Seek input from other professionals.

- Identify hazards before you start flying.

- Define the goal of the mission.

- Crawl, walk, run.

- Develop exit strategies.

- Practice exit strategies before the complete maneuver/mission.

- Start in ideal conditions and work towards limits.

- Take on only those risks required by the goal.

- Take on only the risks for which you have trained.

- Check your work; make sure things are working as planned.

Visit Chuck Aaron's YouTube channel to see him in action.

DARING TO DREAM:
The Analytical & Technological Process of Making the Impossible Happen

APSCON 2019 coincided with two significant aviation events that consumed conversation among show attendees. One was the 50th anniversary of Apollo 11. If you want to see the eyes of a tough, steely-eyed aviator shimmer with tears, show him a manned rocket launch. The Apollo missions offered so many lessons in aeronautical professionalism, risk management and engineering achievement, we are still studying them half a century later. The second event was about an upcoming movie. Walking around the expo, I would randomly hear a familiar tune: the theme from *Top Gun*. Upon finding the source of the music, I would see two to six adults huddled closely around a phone or laptop looking like children on Christmas Eve. Yes, the *Top Gun: Maverick* trailer was released.

Why compare the Apollo 11 anniversary to one of the most aeronautically inaccurate flying movies of all time? Stay on my wing, Mav. I'll explain.

A high-altitude Indian Air Force SAR unit uses the following motto: "We do the difficult as routine. The impossible may take a bit longer."

Our industry has a long history of doing what society believes is impossible. On Oct. 22, 1903, a prominent scientist, Professor Simon Newcomb, published an article explaining that if a man could get off the ground, he could never land. "Once he slackens his speed, down he begins to fall," Newcomb wrote. "Once he stops, he falls a dead mass.

How shall he reach the ground without destroying his delicate machinery? I do not think that even the most imaginative inventor has yet even put on paper a demonstrative, successful way of meeting this difficulty. May not our [engineers] be ultimately forced to admit that aerial flight is one of the great problems with which man can never cope, and give up all attempts to grapple with it?"

Two months later, the Wright Brothers flew at Kitty Hawk. Afterward, many newspapers refused to cover the story because they believed the flight to be not just improbable, but absolutely impossible. The idea of two bicycle makers with no college education or major financial backing accomplishing the task was considered nonsense.

The Wright Brothers lead to a series of other impossible accomplishments from aeronautical pioneers, including the outside loop and breaking the sonic barrier. Jimmy Doolittle, Chuck Yeager and the teams behind them made quick work of both mental roadblocks. We have filled volumes of books of such accomplishments over the last 100 years of aerospace. A long history of repeatedly rewriting what people can and cannot do has become one of the greatest sources of inspiration in our world.

While the world watches in awe at these conquests over nature, we rarely understand how they happen. Long hours of study and controlled experimentation do not make it into the movies. We are, therefore, led to believe such incredible power over the laws of nature comes from brazen men and women who disregard rules and throw themselves against the wind, fueled by unbridled bravery. It makes for great entertainment, but it is a dangerous misconception.

Apollo 11 was a phoenix rising from the ashes of Apollo 1. Prior to the Apollo program, NASA had been taking measured steps toward increasingly complex space travel. The administration took the time to engineer and test spacecraft used in missions that slowly added skills, such as docking two vehicles and space walking.

The Apollo program did not have the luxury of a measured approach. President Kennedy's "end of the decade" decree put pressure on NASA to design the spacecraft and train crews quickly. The constant fear Russia would beat the U.S. to the moon added to the urgency. By the time Apollo 1 was nearing operational readiness tests, President Johnson was looking for a positive public relations story to take attention away from the escalating war in Vietnam and civil rights unrest back home. The message to NASA was clear: The department needed to put Apollo 1 in the air ASAP.

At the beginning of 1967, Apollo 1 reported more than 20,000 documented mechanical and electrical problems, including serious issues with the communications systems and flight simulator. The problems continued to plague the "plugs-out" test on Jan. 27. While the first test was normally conducted without crew, NASA decided to jump ahead to a crewed test with launch only a month away. So many problems arose with the capsule during countdown, the engineers suggested cancelling the rest of the test. The suggestion was ignored, and a suspected short circuit ignited the oxygen in the capsule, killing Gus Grissom, Ed White and Roger Chaffee.

In a twist of fate, the one item that did work as designed was the crew door. It had been redesigned after the door on a Gemini capsule inadvertently blew open during recovery, causing the spacecraft to sink in the ocean. The door was reengineered so it would not come open accidently, and the emergency explosive charges were removed. The new door would open inward and take more than 90 seconds to do so. The design ensured the crew could not escape the compartment quickly in Apollo 1. The astronaut on the Gemini flight, which led to the hatch redesign, was Grissom.

The Russians were under the same pressure in the space race. Eighty-six days after the Apollo 1 tragedy, cosmonaut Vladimir Komarov blasted off in a new Soyuz spacecraft. Like Apollo 1, Komarov's vehicle had been pushed through the design, production and testing phases. And like Apollo 1, the Soyuz was infested with problems. Major control system failures made safe reentry into the atmosphere seem impossible. But Komarov managed to manually align the craft and reenter through sheer skill. Unfortunately, the recovery parachutes failed to open properly and he died on impact.

No amount of operational need, bravery or administrative pressure can overpower engineering. We do make the impossible happen, but we do it by following an analytical process of thinking through problems, designing solutions and testing them to ensure they work.

When George Low took over the Apollo program in 1967, he knew the solutions would take as long they would take—no less. Low was an engineer and interested in effective solutions, not schedules. He turned the initial 12-month timetable into 21 months before he was satisfied and sent the next Apollo mission up. "Once a question is asked, once a problem is identified, a solution can always be found," Low later said. "In space, we are successful because we are curious, because we look for answers. And whenever we did have a failure, the reason was always the same: We had failed to be inquisitive."

The business of aviation does not forgive arrogance, ignorance or negligence. Sometimes, we receive a humbling slap in the face. Other times, we become a tragic lesson for others. If we wish to bend the laws of nature and redefine what is possible, we must commit ourselves to the diligent work required to complete the task. If it is not hard work, we are probably doing it wrong.

How can one stay motivated enough to consistently work hard while pushing against the limitations of the world as we know it? Through the same inspiration aviation creates in all people. Be excited about the pure magic involved in what we do. Love that our jobs define the extremities of humanity's imagination. Revel in the fact that "impossible" is a challenge for us, not a limit.

"No amount of operational need, bravery or administrative pressure can overpower engineering. We do make the impossible happen, but we do it by following an analytical process of thinking through problems, designing solutions and testing them to ensure they work."

"[Aeronautical] research should be defined as doing something that half of the people think is impossible," said Burt Rutan, the embodiment of aeronautical imagination. "So what that means is that a true creative researcher has to have confidence in nonsense."

Yes, *Top Gun* and movies like it inaccurately show how aviation makes the impossible routine business. If we forget the importance of taking the proper steps, even the smartest and most skilled among us can fall to disaster. However, the magic of our industry is absolutely breathtaking, and it's okay for us to be in love with it—such inspiration is what fuels us so we can do the difficult work needed to live on the edge of the world's technological limits.

Let the magic of aviation fuel you up. After *Top Gun* came out in 1986, I had a closet full of white t-shirts and jeans to complement my brown leather jacket. Yes, the movie is chalk full of factual errors. But if I'm anywhere and a TV is playing *Top Gun*—or any good flying movie— I will stop in my tracks and watch, because they have successfully captured the feeling of aviation.

Be inspired, be excited, work hard and be methodical about the work you have chosen to do, especially in an industry that considers "impossible" a dare.

UA232:
What History Can Teach Us About Crew Resource Management

A mere five sentences in the National Transportation Safety Board report DCA89MA063 summarize one of the most significant events in aviation history.

"On July 19, 1989, at 1516, a DC-10-10, N1819U, operated by United Airlines as flight 232, experienced a catastrophic failure of the No. 2 tail-mounted engine during cruise flight. The separation, fragmentation and forceful discharge of stage 1 fan rotor assembly parts from the No. 2 engine led to the loss of the three hydraulic systems that powered the airplane's flight controls. The flight crew experienced severe difficulties controlling the airplane, which subsequently crashed during an attempted landing at Sioux Gateway Airport, Iowa. There were 285 passengers and 11 crewmembers onboard. One flight attendant and 110 passengers were fatally injured."

The flight is famous because of the heroic actions of Captain Al Haynes, Captain Dennis Finch, First Officer William Records and Second Officer Dudley Dvorak. The crew managed what was previously deemed an "impossible" system failure, under equally impossible odds for survival. And the event is important because it is one of the earliest and most powerful examples of the benefits of crew resource management (CRM).

Unfortunately, Haynes made his final flight west in 2019, but the lessons he passed on will continue to keep aircrews safe for as long as we are wise enough to remember them. I'd like to do my part to help us all remember.

The term CRM has been rebranded by countless people to push different angles of the complex topic. The common thread is CRM involves using all resources available to effectively deal with a challenge and achieve the optimal result.

CRM applies equally to maintenance personnel and UAS operating teams as to aircrews. While CRM is a skill, it is based on established best practices and knowledge obtained before an incident arises. Without aircrew training, CRM cannot function. The four aircrew members in the cockpit of United Airlines flight 232 (UA232) had a combined 87,967 flight hours. Haynes had 29,967 of the hours himself.

We should want everyone in our aircrew to play a part in critical situations. We can put our own crews through hours and hours of CRM training by the best instructors in the business. However, without training on the skills and techniques involved in the job they must perform, they will have no resources to manage.

Depending on what you fly, have you taught your TFOs about basic aerodynamics so they understand loss of tail rotor effectiveness, vortex ring state or stalls/spins? Does the crew chief in the back know what a hydraulics failure will do to the aircraft? Do your UAS visual observers know about lost data link or flyaway issues the aircraft may encounter? Do your junior maintenance staff members understand how human factors impact errors in aircraft repairs? As Bob Hoover once said, "You can't pull a rabbit out of a hat unless you put it there first." We cannot afford to make people part of our teams without giving them comprehensive training on all aspects of the job. Only then will we have resources to manage during operations.

The NTSB report on UA232 offers a few details, including: "A flight attendant advised the captain that a UAL DC-10 training check airman, who was off duty and seated in a passenger seat, had volunteered his assistance. The captain immediately invited the airman to the cockpit."

The focus in many CRM courses is on how to manage resources. Before we start managing, we must accept the fact that using additional resources will lead to a better result and use them. This is easier said than done, especially with the type-A population dominating public safety aviation. All the resources in the world and the best resource management skills possible will make zero impact if we do not make the active decision to put CRM in play.

Listening to the audiotape from UA232, you do not hear a captain barking orders to the crew. What you hear is a conversation between crewmembers right to the end of the tape. The conversation is what facilitated the correct actions the crew took to save lives that day.

Think you have this mastered? It is easy to imagine during what I call "Big Red Light" emergencies—the ones accompanied by lights announcing engine failures, fires, etc. But CRM does not start and stop when the big red lights go off. It starts the minute you meet your team for the workday and continues to the end. It is there while you prepare for the shift, when you do the mundane chores of your job and afterward during postflight and cleanup. If CRM is not healthy during normal times, it will not survive emergencies. Think of it like exercise: You cannot expect to run a marathon today if you haven't exercised in months.

We must ask ourselves if we are using CRM during normal procedures. Are we willing to ask for and listen to input from our team on a regular basis? Do we look for or avoid involving others in routine tasks? Are we willing to ask for help when needed? For most of us, including me, initiating and accepting assistance from others is a skill that needs work. But where trained crews are involved, "we" will always produce better results than "me."

How about systems and avionics? They are a resource available in the cockpit, and many of us are not as proficient at managing them as we should be. If CRM is important, we must be completely comfortable with the avionics in front of us, including their basic and advanced functions. Do you have an autopilot or stability augmentation system? Are you comfortable using it? Unfamiliarity with basic avionics has been a contributing factor in many fatal accidents.

On UA232, the crew spent a considerable amount of time troubleshooting aircraft systems. Through the crewmembers' understanding of the systems, they were able to devise a plan to bring the airplane under enough control to attempt a landing, despite having no hydraulics for flight controls or flaps and the ability only to turn right.

Once we have resources in place and the willingness to use them, can we get to the business of managing them? One last barrier may apply: CRM requires a certain amount of human performance to work. If the power required by the situation exceeds the power available from the people involved, the CRM engine will not start, no matter how good it is. Limitations like fatigue, stress, illness and nutrition can sabotage CRM training and skills.

One of the most critical parts of a healthy CRM program is a flight risk assessment tool, which accounts for the level of human performance to be expected from a crew. No amount of training, determination or good intentions can overcome basic human factors.

So, your CRM is finally is in place and functioning. Some basic CRM skills include tasking assignments and workload management, clear communication with crosschecking, appropriate assertiveness and inquiries, situational awareness and adjusting to changes in the environment. The skills are presented in CRM training classes, but they must be perfected in scenario-based training. They are also the same basic skills needed by a crew to accomplish assigned tasks and mission goals. CRM is not just for emergencies.

Safety and effectiveness are complementary in public safety aviation. Nowhere is that more obvious than in CRM. Great CRM leads to captured bad guys, rescued lost persons, controlled wildfires and well-maintained aircraft.

The award-winning missions and videos we enjoy at APSCON every year highlight what trained multi-person crews are capable of doing. The accident database on the APSA website shows CRM is equally influential when it comes to safety. Approximately 70 percent of non-training accidents in our industry involve aircraft without a second trained crewmember in the cockpit. In short, thanks to CRM, the safest crews are also the most effective crews.

The end of NTSB's report on UA232 says, "The Safety Board believes that under the circumstances, the UAL flight crew performance was highly commendable and greatly exceeded reasonable expectations."

I suspect the performance displayed in the incident simply highlighted, in spectacular fashion, the professionalism that was already routine for Haynes and his crew.

May we all be wise enough to remember to try to do the same every day we are honored to do the jobs we do.

THE THIN BLUE LINE:
What Safety Lessons Can You Learn From A Fallen Officer

Public safety aviators are not careless daredevils seeking danger simply for the thrill of it. Most of us agree to take on the risks of the job because we know it is for the good of others. When one of our peers is lost to tragedy, we are left to carry that responsibility for them. To that end, we can learn from such tragedies and keep others from falling victim to the same circumstances.

We often fail to learn from tragedy because we are concerned that addressing the facts of the incident will somehow tarnish the names of those involved. But when we refuse to talk about an accident, we refuse to honor the deal the fallen officer made on the first day of the job: to risk his life for the betterment of others.

On Oct. 15, 2010, Sergeant Joe Schuengel of the Missouri State Highway Patrol was returning to base after dropping off two passengers. His Bell 206B crash landed on a roadway a short time into the flight. Schuengel was killed. In early 2012, the National Transportation Safety Board released its final report on the incident. Looking for more information,

I called Schuengel's colleagues at the Missouri State Highway Patrol and a nearby law enforcement aviation unit where he parked his helicopter. Every person I spoke to had nothing but positive things to say about Schuengel, both personally and professionally.

From a safety point of view, it is not so important what Schuengel did or did not do. What is important are the questions raised by the incident. What factors may have contributed to the accident? How can those factors influence the safety of others?

NTSB determined the probable causes to be "the total loss of engine power due to fuel exhaustion, which resulted from the pilot's inadequate preflight planning and decision making, and his improper control inputs following the loss of engine power, which resulted in mast bumping and separation of the main rotor. Contributing to the accident was the pilot's improper judgment in acting as a pilot with disqualifying medical conditions." Let's look at each of these issues one at a time.

Fuel exhaustion is one of the first accident causes our primary flight instructors address. In addition, many of us fly the same type of aircraft—if not the same aircraft—day in and day out, developing a keen sense of the fuel system and consumption rate. According to the Aircraft Owners and Pilots Association (AOPA) 2011 Nall Report, the fuel exhaustion accident rate has declined by 50 percent over the last 10 years. Still, in the past few months, I have read about two law enforcement fuel exhaustion accidents (one helicopter and one light sport aircraft). AOPA still attributes 6-8 percent of all general aviation accidents to this cause. According to an International Helicopter Safety Team report, of the fuel exhaustion related accidents analyzed, the average time of the accident pilot was 5,748 hours, with more than 1,200 hours in make and model.

All of this data indicates experience can work against us. More than a few pilots consider the ability to fly an aircraft as dry as possible without crashing a mark of experience. I have talked with TFOs who told me their pilots routinely use the low fuel light as the return to base indicator. Disturbingly, the TFOs typically attributed the fact that the pilot's flight experience allowed him to push the aircraft further than more junior pilots.

As we become increasingly comfortable with the fuel gauge needle sitting close to empty, we allow more and more risk to creep into our fuel planning. It doesn't happen overnight; it is a slow process. And when the day comes that the engine quits, it is a surprise, even for pilots who know how much fuel is in the tanks on takeoff and how much the aircraft will burn.

In the case of the Missouri State Highway Patrol accident, the pilot had 2,600 hours, including 800 in the Bell 206B, and knew his fuel was low, telling his passengers he would not be able to fly them as long as usual before dropping them off. As they departed the aircraft, Schuengel told the passengers he had only a 10-minute flight back to the airport. One of the passengers noted the fuel gauge was halfway between empty and 25 gallons. It is impossible to know exactly how much was left in the tanks when he started home, but it is reasonable to assume the aircraft was low on fuel.

Many of us are guilty of cutting it as close as Schuengel did that day, but it cannot be allowed. One reason is neither the math nor equipment is reliable when the needle is that close to empty. Most of us start with a fuel load that allows at least two to three hours of flight time, if not more. Using a rough estimate of the fuel burn provides only a moderate level of accuracy. We have to assume the actual burn can be off several gallons per hour when we are in the air. When that error builds up over several hours, the reserve we originally estimated to be at a certain number of gallons at the end of the flight may be significantly depleted. When we have an hour of fuel left in the tanks, this error is not significant. But when we are dealing with the small amounts of fuel single-engine aircraft can use as a reserve, it can disappear quickly. Imagine we have an error of 2 gallons per hour over two hours in an aircraft that only requires 6 gallons for a 20-minute reserve.

The fuel gauges in our aircraft cannot be taken as gospel. They should be considered advisory. In many aircraft in the law enforcement community, the gauge is only accurate when the aircraft is level. We are rarely level. Years ago, while working an active manhunt, I pushed our fuel to what I felt was a safe reserve and then raced to a nearby airport to fill up, hoping to get back on-scene quickly. I was paying more attention to the fuel gauge than usual, and as we approached the ramp to land, I lamented that we could have stayed on the call for a few more minutes because we had more fuel than I thought. When I put the skids on the ground, leveling the aircraft for the first time in hours, the low fuel light immediately popped on and the fuel gauge dropped. I got chills. Luck had facilitated an important lesson that I never forgot.

We should also refresh ourselves on how much of the remaining fuel shown on the gauge is actually useable and do a zero-fuel weight and balance. Are you still within the center of gravity limits with minimum fuel and your standard crew?

A second factor in the Missouri State Highway Patrol incident we should consider is the medical condition raised by the report. How many of us have let a medical issue go undisclosed or even untreated because we did not want to lose our flight status? How many of us have taken medication and not told anyone for the same reason? This does not need to be a chronic ailment; pushing our self-assessment on a cold or flu can be just as deadly.

An FAA medical examiner once handed me my completed annual examination form, which includes a disclosure of all doctor visits and illnesses over the past three years, and jokingly said, "Here's a copy to keep your story straight for next year." We laughed, but he was right. The thought of letting the government know about a medical issue scares many of us more than the thought of a crash. The situation is dangerous and too widespread to ignore.

Schuengel did not leave his medical condition untreated. The medication he was taking required a prescription, which indicates he saw a doctor. Taking the initiative to seek medical attention instead of ignoring the situation deserves due credit and is more than many of us do. However, a family physician is unlikely to have the kind of knowledge in aviation physiology necessary to make a reliable decision on how your health or the medications you are taking will affect your ability to safely fly a law enforcement mission. We must make sure we address our medical issues, but we must also make sure we ask the right questions of the right people.

Finally, there is the conclusion of NTSB that mast-bumping led to the separation of the main rotor. The report attributes the mast bump to the pilot's, "improper control inputs following the loss of engine power." While this is one possible scenario, anytime we subject a semi-rigid rotor system to zero or negative G-loading, we set the stage for mast bumping. Many possible scenarios can lead to mast bumping, and we have no record of what happened in the cockpit prior to its occurrence in Schuengel's aircraft. A negative G pushover following loss of engine power is an area that needs to be addressed in training. The psychological desire to point the nose of an aircraft at the nearest landing spot following an unexpected loss of engine power can be difficult to contain. It is similar to the strong impulse to pull the cyclic aft and slow the helicopter while sliding on the ground despite knowing it will only chop off the tail boom. Flight instructors are constantly pushing against the cyclic to keep pilots from pulling back on a ground run, even with experienced aviators. Usually, the pilot does not know he or she is doing it unless the instructor mentions it.

These are issues that can only be addressed in training, and only practice will allow us to ignore these urges and respond as we have been trained. Many of the flight instructors I have interviewed on increasing safety in our industry have said they think more training needs to be conducted on the entry and stabilization of an autorotation. We usually spend quite a bit of time on the flare and touchdown (real or simulated to a hover), but if we do not enter the auto correctly, everything afterwards will be negatively affected. I believe this extends to the fixed-wing arena, as well. When was the last time most fixed-wing or rotorcraft pilots practiced an engine failure from an orbit? Do you relate your readiness to perform an emergency maneuver to your currency or your proficiency? Hopefully, you do both.

Three separate factors were listed by NTSB as contributing to the

Missouri State Highway Patrol incident: fuel planning, autorotation entry and medical factors. If we were able to go back in time and remove just one of those, the incident could have ended differently. Here is where we can make the most significant impact on our current safety culture. If we learn to recognize the potentially lethal nature of seemingly acceptable risks combined with other factors, we can remove ingredients from the accident formula.

Look back at the three risk factors raised in this case and consider how you might have viewed them if they were addressed separately. Consider how seriously you would have taken the threat these issues pose if they were not addressed in the context of a fatal accident involving an experienced, well-liked law enforcement pilot. These are common issues within our profession. Most of the people reading this can personally relate to at least one aspect of this accident. On Oct. 15, 2010, several of these all-too common risks piled up at once and led to tragedy.

SOLUTIONS & STRENGTH:
What A Good SMS Can Provide

Safety management systems (SMS) are not perfect. Implementing them in the real world, especially the public safety aviation industry, can be difficult. Often, we fail to properly train safety officers, managers and staff. Sometimes, we attempt to fit SMS characteristics from other industries directly into ours, only to be frustrated by incompatibilities. We get too focused on documents and policies.

I have heard a number of arguments that SMS do not work because accidents still occur. It was even suggested that SMS might increase risk by distracting safety efforts from more meaningful tasks. One of the alternatives offered to installing SMS is to double down on efforts to hire the right people.

Labeling pilots, TFOs or mechanics who make mistakes as flawed and making their removal the solution to our problems is not the kind of safety currency we want to bank on. Sometimes, there are people who just shouldn't be doing these jobs. More often, however, mistakes are a bad combination of "human performance required" and "human performance available" at the moment they occur. These are factors that vary for all of us. Our job requires fluctuating levels of brainpower. An increase in the number of opportunities for failure demands more concentration at various points in our day, and other factors affect how focused we might feel.

According to APSA Aeromedical Liaison Dudley Crosson, variance in human performance is akin to GPS navigation systems. For top performance, the GPS is designed to receive information from a set number of satellites. At times we lose the signal from one or more of the satellites, reducing the performance of the GPS. If we are flying in good weather, degraded performance is not a big deal. However, if we lose that same performance level while shooting a WAAS approach to minimums in IFR conditions, loss of a satellite may be the difference between success and failure.

For each of us, performance is based on getting enough rest, food and water, and maintaining good mental health, perception and experience, among other factors. At times, we may not have the resources or information needed to optimize our capabilities.

"Even your best employees will have a fight with a spouse or a bad night of sleep from time to time and lose a satellite or two, Crosson said. "To expect that they will always be operating at 100 percent is unrealistic."

For this reason, putting all of our eggs in the "hire people who make good decisions" basket is guaranteed to fail at some point.

The key is to hire those people, then offer some protection from their own limitations. This is true for the operation or maintenance of any aircraft, from a large multi-engine to a lightweight UAS.

Consider a classic aircraft performance chart showing the relationship between power available and power required. Such charts typically show changes in the two variables. A pilot learns to perform only the maneuvers that can be supported by the power available from the aircraft. Failure to respect this law of flight most commonly leads to loss of control incidents. This usually occurs where the two lines on the chart cross each other and power required meets or exceeds power available.

Those same two variables can be replaced by human performance available at any moment in time and human performance required to complete a task. "Knowing" oneself is a great way to keep from getting into a position of performance deficit, but it is far from perfect. Often, the state of lowered human performance itself makes it difficult to perceive and identify the situation. A fatigued person is a poor evaluator of his or her own fatigue level. What's more, we might already be in the middle of an activity when we "lose a couple satellites" and have no choice but to continue in a less than optimum state.

Another theory to help us understand this issue is Dr. Daniel Kahneman's "Theory of Attention." The theory has been used as a basis for research in decision-making since Kahneman's initial publication in the early 1970s. The idea is that we have a limited amount of cognitive ability that can be allocated toward tasks put in front of us at any given time. Every task takes a bit of those cognitive resources out—some more than others. Once we run out, performance will decrease. There are things we can do to influence how big the bucket is, such as training and experience. Fatigue, stress, nutrition, etc. also influence how full the bucket is.

Kahneman also addresses the importance of attention itself. Even if we are skilled at a task, unless it holds our attention, the resources directed at it will be inefficient. Either not enough cognitive power will be directed at it, or it will not be addressed in an efficient manner, draining more resources than it should. In other words, if you don't think something is important or interesting, you will perform poorly, even if you know how to do the task well.

Yet our typical response to human error is still to point a finger and say, "make better decisions" or "don't fly if you shouldn't be flying." Employees sit through the same safety training year after year, no matter how boring it is, with the expectation that performance will automatically increase. We continue to do this and wonder why there is little change in the accident rate or causal factors.

I am not saying that we should stop trying to hire the right people and train on decision-making skills. Quite the opposite, I think we should add more material to that curriculum—specifically SMS training. SMS can provide the safety net needed to predict, identify and mitigate periods when our performance falls below task requirements. If you think about your aircraft, you know what the red line limits are. There are likely lights, alarms and soothing computer voices to tell you when those limits are about to be exceeded. How do you know your safety limits?

Human performance changes and the level of performance required of aircrew members varies throughout the shift/day/week. There will be periods where these two levels intersect, and these are the times when an incident is likely to happen. Usually, we do not realize we've entered this dangerous zone until something happens to clearly illustrate we are in over our head. Often, it is already too late for corrective action. What we want is to be able to identify and predict when we will approach our performance limits so we can stop while we still have a choice. SMS can provide a barrier against those performance limits.

This is why we do risk assessments through SMS. We identify the hazards and likely scenarios that produce the highest risk. We focus on the point where ability is likely to fall below performance requirements. When done right, we look at ways to identify these high-risk points and change the course of events. It is this process, this integration into all operational tasks that makes it a true "system."

Too often, when asked about an organization's SMS, we are presented with a manual. If the system isn't a seamless part of operations, training and maintenance, it will fail to prevent an accident, and the detractors to this method of risk management will be proven correct.

Safety can be boring, and this can make it hard to keep our attention. As we saw above, the inability to captivate our attention makes a task difficult to do correctly. Too often, in training and safety, we randomly pick out topics to address. That disconnect with our daily lives makes these efforts seem irrelevant. Closely connecting safety information to real safety issues in a practical and meaningful way cures this failure. Safety officers must make the information as interesting as possible. Pictures, videos and even a bit of comedy go a long way.

SMS are not intended to replace good hiring practices or training. They are meant to supplement those efforts. They are not meant to replace good decision-making, knowledge or experience. Often, people are offended at the suggestion that SMS do the thinking for them. SMS are tools that can help each of us better utilize our skills and sound judgment to do our jobs better. You shouldn't be any more offended at SMS than you are by warning and caution lights on your instrument panel. They are both performing the same service.

Of course, these benefits are dependent on SMS being implemented correctly. Fortunately, SMS have a built in component that allows us to know the answer to that question. Safety assurance is a means of tracking performance. Unfortunately, it is often missing or poorly implemented by many organizations claiming to have SMS. Wondering if your system is performing safety assurance? Look at the last safety program report. It should show performance of risk controls, participation of employees in the system, changes in risk, etc. If you do not have such a report, you've answered the question quite clearly. Poor implementation usually can be attributed to inadequate training and/or insufficient managerial support.

The sub-par implementation of SMS in some cases should not be interpreted as the systems being poor risk management solutions. SMS installed poorly will give poor results. Done correctly, however, they can bring safety in our industry to the next level by offering solutions to the accident causes that seem to remain the same year after year.

REAL-WORLD FACTORS INFLUENCE DECISION MAKING

Do you know that it is risky to fly when you are tired? Do you need someone to tell you it is dangerous to fly a VFR aircraft into weather conditions that are likely to become IFR? Were you aware that it is unwise to fly an aircraft or perform a maintenance task unless you have had proper and current training? So the question is, why? We all answered "yes" to the questions above, right? We know what causes aircraft accidents. We know the dangers of fatigue, lack of training, weather, improper responses to mechanical failures and the other items listed in FRATs and addressed by safety management systems. Do they think we need their help realizing not to fly if those conditions exist?

Now, honestly answer the following questions. Have you ever flown in weather that you later realized you shouldn't have? Have you ever been too tired, sick or mentally stressed to fly but went anyway? Ever made an approach to land a little fast because you were looking nervously at your low fuel level? Ever sit in a chair after a flight, quietly mad at yourself for making a dumb decision or oversight, knowing good fortune saved your butt again?

Every pilot, TFO and mechanic has done something wrong because they didn't know any better. However, we all have also done things we knew we shouldn't have been doing. In many cases, it's not due to a lack of training, intelligence or sense of responsibility. Often, it is because the decision-making framework we establish in our books and presentations does not work flawlessly outside the classroom. Sometimes, real-world factors influence our ability to apply what we know to be correct, leading us to instead believe what we wish to be true.

There are many models for the decision-making process. All of them require one common element in order to make it to an intended outcome (i.e. not crashing): situational awareness (SA). Without a functional understanding of what is happening and how it will influence the future, we cannot make effective decisions that will get the results we are aiming for, no matter how smart we are.

SA can be lost due to one or more of three problems: 1) We fail to detect information about the situation around us. 2) The information about our environment is perceived, but we fail to correctly interpret, understand or accept it. 3) The situation is perceived and understood correctly; however, we do not properly project how the current situation will influence the future.

As the HEMS world is well aware, one major factor that can lead to a breakdown in SA is the presence of a passenger. The three major accidents referenced by NTSB in its 2015 report on public safety aviation all involved aircraft that had a passenger onboard. The VIP transport industry has a notorious history of accidents with famous musicians on board. Stevie Ray Vaughan died in a helicopter crash on Aug. 27, 1990. Otis Redding recorded his Motown hit "Sittin' on the Dock of the Bay" three days before he and his band were killed in a Beechcraft H18. Patsy Cline, "Cowboy" Copas and Hawkshaw Hawkins of Grand Ole Opry fame all died in a Piper PA-24 Comanche leaving a benefit concert for another artist who had been killed. And of course, there is "The Day the Music Died," when Buddy Holly, J.P. Richardson (the Big Bopper) and Ritchie Valens were killed in a Bonanza.

In addition to involving influential musicians, all of these crashes were attributed to inclement weather. In other words, these legends all died because the pilot they entrusted with their safety chose to fly into weather he or she shouldn't have. Surely we wouldn't make the same mistake, right? They must have had some gap in their training where they should have learned flying VFR into bad weather is not safe.

A study published by the University of Illinois looked at causal factors in IIMC accidents. One interesting piece of data the researchers uncovered was that when compared to other accident types, IIMC accidents were more likely—54 percent more likely—to occur with a passenger on board. Additionally, they found that "approximately 76 percent of VFR-IMC accidents appeared to involve intentional flight into adverse weather."

In public safety aviation, we do not routinely have passengers aboard unless tasked with transport or HEMS responsibilities. This does not isolate us from the findings in this report. The infrequency of having passengers makes this type of mission special. Often, our passengers are commanding officers, agency heads, VIPs, injured patients or SWAT, K9 or rescue dive team personnel. The rest of the time, when we think it is just the TFO and pilot in the aircraft, the radio brings passengers into the cockpit with us. Sometimes, the radio can make it seem like we have the entire upper echelon of the agency in the backseat. All of these factors can add to the desire to complete the mission even in the face of obvious safety issues.

A passenger can cause us to fail to "detect information about the situation around us" due to the imposed desire to complete the mission with which they are associated. This is no less a factor in any maintenance task. Confirmation bias is the tendency to perceive and focus on only those things that support what we expect or want to believe. If there is hazard information around us that does not help satisfy the goal, we may subconsciously fail to recognize its existence.

Part of the correct interpretation of situational information involves relating that perception to the correct experiences and training. Again, if that experience or knowledge is contrary to the mission at hand, we may fail to make the connection between what we are seeing and what we know it means.

Even if we manage to sense and understand the situation around us right now, conflict with our goals and the goals of our passengers can lead to denial of the projected path. This can lead us to blindly continue into situations we know are unsafe simply because we don't want to believe the most likely outcome will occur. How many accident reports have we read that fit this description? Too many.

None of the three failures in SA listed above have anything to do with the pilot, TFO or maintenance technician not having the proper knowledge, training or experience needed to sense, understand, project and respond to hazards. The issue is the failure to perceive, interpret and project, not the inability to do so. These failures in SA may sound familiar to you. They have been covered many times, usually with advice such as, "Don't let external pressures affect your decision to fly," "Remember that you have the final authority to say no," "Don't get too caught up in the mission," and so on. Still, pilots who have heard this advice over and over again through many years of service still fall victim to this sneaky killer. Why?

One reason is that while all of that advice sounds great when sitting in a conference room, when an officer you used to work the road with comes under gunfire and is screaming for an aircraft, or when a 3-year-old goes missing right after you called your child to say goodnight, your situational awareness is likely to be negatively influenced. And it's not just heart-pounding calls. Routine from doing the same job for a long period of time tends to change in slow, undetectable ways. Those subtle changes can trim away vital tasks that erode SA in a way that is extremely difficult to detect. Time pressures can also degrade our ability to collect all of the information needed for good SA. Usually, people need us five minutes ago. This leaves us focused on collecting only the information we deem necessary for the mission, which can inadvertently leave out important elements needed for a complete picture of the situation. These losses in SA can affect all of us, regardless of knowledge level.

Good decision making skills let us apply all of our training, knowledge and expertise to reach our goals. SA is the avenue that allows us to connect this knowledge and the decision making process. Too often, we assume an accident was caused by a pilot or technician's lack of training or decision making skills. In our line of work, however, it is frequently because there was a short between the two caused by a loss of SA. Sometimes our initial reaction to new safety ideas that address decision making is to counterattack the suggestion that we need help in making safe choices. It is an understandable response by professionals who pride themselves on being skilled at making such decisions.

The tools and techniques suggested by FAA, NTSB, PSAAC and other safety professionals are not intended to fix some lack of ability to make safe decisions. They address the conditions that sometimes lead to a failure to apply those abilities. They are meant to be tools to help us see through the fog of chaos in which we sometimes operate and apply, in an accurate and effective manner, our knowledge and experience. It is not something that should take decisions away from the operator. Instead, it should be like adding sights to a weapon in order to help us utilize our skills more effectively to hit our targets.

THE PUBLIC SAFETY PROFESSIONAL:
Strive to Lower Risks & Achieve Better Results

It is unfortunate that so many in our profession see safety as a ball and chain. Often, it is because what law enforcement considers risk management in general has little to do with operational safety. We start to believe anything that carries the labels of "safety" and "risk management" are, at best, necessary evils that will always have a negative impact on our ability to do our jobs effectively.

Sometimes, we think of operations and safety as being on a balance, like the scales of justice. But with this approach, the two elements are in opposition. We keep them separated with different manuals, personnel and meetings. What if there was a different way? The most professional tactics, training and management techniques deliver both lower risk and better results. It is not about safety being first or the mission taking priority; it is about being professional, first and foremost, without exception. If we do that, safety and operational results will follow.

When we consider how to operate more safely, we often first think about how we conduct actual missions. What altitudes, airspeeds, crew configurations and tactics do we use? The tactics that offer the highest probability of success also carry the lowest risk.

Higher altitudes, based on the maximum effective range of the system you are operating, offer better viewpoints and angles for suspect and missing person searches, surveillance and pursuits. Higher altitudes allow us to maximize the capabilities of a camera system, such as providing a more stable image with a slower rotational speed, and yield a more effective search. It is also easier to confuse and influence suspects if they are not sure where you are looking, as opposed to maintaining eye contact with them from rooftop level.

In addition to the tactical advantages, higher altitude flight profiles offer more time to react to emergencies, open more landing site options, lower the likelihood of loss of aircraft control, and reduce wire, bird and ground-fire strike probabilities. The procedures are not safety-driven burdens crews have learned to make the best of. Professional operators use the flight profiles not only because they are safer, but also because they produce the best results.

To achieve professional results, we have to train like professionals. Great pilots, TFOs, mechanics, medics, remote pilots and crew chiefs are not born; they are made through training.

The training needed to be a great public safety aircrew member goes beyond patrol officer experience or passing a commercial pilot exam. The same goes for someone with a fresh A&P license. He or she still needs extensive training on equipment, airframes and the unique challenges of maintaining public safety aircraft. Passing a remote pilot exam and buying a UAS does not equip anyone with the skills needed to be an effective public safety UAS operator.

A professional curriculum for any public safety aviation position must include knowledge and skills that reduce risk while simultaneously increasing operational efficiency. Analysis of the APSA accident database shows more than 70 percent of operational public safety aviation accidents (i.e. non-training flights) occur when the aircraft is operated either single pilot or without a trained second crewmember.

The crew coordination needed to effectively manage a mission involves the same resource management skills needed to maintain a high level of safety. Unit members who communicate effectively will squeeze more production out of their resources and time than others.

Crew resource management is not just about safety, and it is not just for emergencies. The communication methods needed to streamline maintenance tasking between maintenance members also reduce errors and improve oversight.

A professional safety management system is not separate from the operational policies and procedures of a unit. An SMS dictates that a unit's operations are conducted in a manner that accounts for risk, just as we account for fuel, maintenance schedules, agency mission tasking, scheduling or any other operational concern. An SMS, implemented properly, helps us successfully complete more missions.

While everyone is quick to say "safety first," too many agencies see safety as a painful drain on funds that could be better spent on operational needs. Given the choice between a techniques and tactics class and a safety class, aircrews are far more likely to sign up for tactics.

We have ourselves to blame for the disconnect between safety and professional success. Too often, our safety training fails to make the connection between the two, and we lose interest.

Scenario-based training is one method to clearly connect safety and professional success. A good scenario combines elements previously separated into either operational skills or safety skills. As our instructors become more versed in safety management, they increase their ability to create better training scenarios. The growing availability of simulator training has helped us offer new training scenarios.

Safety training and education increases professionalism, which in turn increases our operational efficiency and mission success, which in turn makes your community a safer place to live. That is what being a public safety aviation professional is all about.

LOVE SAFETY:
5 Reasons You Should Embrace the Safe

Why do we hate "safety" so much? Just saying the word, more often than not, prompts comments and poorly disguised jokes, ranging from boredom to disdain. The announcement of an airborne tactics class brings cheers rarely heard when a safety course is scheduled. We congratulate those who become chief pilots and offer sympathies to new safety officers. Even if we are honestly interested in safety, we still joke about how terrible it is.

How did we get like this? Is it innocent joking, or does it hurt us? There are many definitions of "safety culture." According to Sky-brary.aero, "Safety Culture is the way safety is perceived, valued and prioritized in an organization."

The *International Helicopter Safety Team SMS Toolkit* has a similar definition, which adds that, "organizations with a positive safety culture are characterized by communications founded on mutual trust, by shared perceptions of the importance of safety and by confidence in the efficacy of preventive measures."

An important concept in both definitions is perception. All of the safety posters, scheduled training, policies and procedures

> "We cannot get past the first step in making our safety program acceptable without understanding what we are trying to accomplish."

reflect, mainly, management's commitment to having a safety program. These things are important, and a safety program cannot survive without involvement from management. However, the perception of employees on the value of these things is critical to producing a safer environment. These negative perceptions come out in our comments and behavior when safety is brought up. No matter how innocent they are, they signify a significant underlying problem. So, why do we hate safety?

1) We Don't Know Why We Are Doing It. Effective safety programs require formal management of the risks in operational tasks. Law enforcement in general does not often do this. According to a study from the University of North Dakota, only 0.039 percent of law enforcement agencies employ risk management as a safety measure. Many think risk management is for agency vehicle crashes, workman's compensation claims, facility conditions or when the agency is sued for damages. When aviation risk management is introduced to public safety, it is often brought from the airlines, military or large commercial operations.

Without consideration for the nuances of public safety aviation, these programs are bulky, expensive, inapplicable and, ultimately, ineffective. Under these conditions, we often assign someone the task of setting up a safety program without the benefit of training. The concepts, methods and even basic terms used in modern safety management are foreign to most law enforcement agencies and public safety aviation. The resources available are rarely a good fit for our type of operations. While we may believe in safety, the process is difficult for everyone to understand. No wonder we dislike the final product.

We cannot get past the first step in making our safety program acceptable without understanding what we are trying to accomplish.

2) Safety Is At Odds With Operations. Aviation professionals in the world of public safety are driven by a desire to do the job with which we have been tasked. Whether it is chasing bad guys, maintaining aircraft, finding lost people, performing rescues or fighting fires, we come to work wanting to do our job because we believe in it. Safety often gets lumped in with other things that keep us from doing our job, such as budget cuts, inept management or aircraft parts availability. Anything that keeps us from doing our job is not met with open arms. Managers want productivity out of aircraft and equipment, and safety seems to keep us from maximizing that.

One reason this battle exists is because we tend to separate the two things. Safety and operations are under different programs, kept in different manuals, addressed in separate meetings, briefed through independent reports. With such a division between operations and safety, it is no wonder they do not complement each other.

Fortunately, we can easily fix this fundamental problem. Safety policies and procedures can be interwoven into the air unit's operations manual instead of being a separate document. Doing a risk assessment for a flight can be as much a part of daily activity as preflighting an aircraft, computing weight and balance or scheduling flights. Safety training can be a part of training, just like annual check rides, initial orientation or quarterly refresher training.

When unit leadership sits down to incorporate safety into the operations manual, many of the conflicts have to be resolved, making safety and operations complementary. We will start to see that not only does safety help us fly more, but it also helps us catch more bad guys and rescue more people.

Crew resource management is a great example of this. Having two or more people in the aircraft who are trained to work together leads to significant increases in mission effectiveness while lowering the likelihood of a human error related accident by up to 70 percent.

Unit policy should outline the composition of a safety committee. The group should include the people responsible for all aspects of the unit's operation. Most safety related policies, procedures and equipment purchases should go through the safety committee. The group effort will lead to better solutions integrated more smoothly into operational needs and training.

Implementation of safety "stuff" without the use of a safety committee almost guarantees conflict with operations. More information on writing safety policies can be found in chapter 1 of the *APSA SMS Installation Guide*.

3) Safety Is Just Someone's Opinion. Often we think safety training, policies and procedures are just someone's opinion of what is "dangerous." Other times we complain because something happened to someone once, and now we are all being punished with a new, restrictive policy. We are right to feel this way, because it is all too often true. Operating safety programs based on assumption is wasteful and irritating.

To fix this problem, we need two things: data and data analysis. We cannot know what to address in our safety program unless we collect information about what the hazards really are. Once we start collecting data, we usually find some of the big problems we thought existed are rare, while smaller problems are more prevalent than we perceived. We can collect data through hazard reports, surveys, inspections, flight risk assessment scores, HUMS, etc.

A big mistake we make after receiving data is to attack it all at once. That can be expensive and time consuming. It is also annoying. Some things have a high likelihood of happening but are not likely to cause much damage—or any at all. Other things could be catastrophic but are not likely to happen. Law enforcement aviation folks are not often impressed with having their hands tied by anything that falls in either of these categories. Doing so also brings us back to the detrimental conflict with operations mentioned earlier.

What if we spent our limited time on those items that had a higher chance of both occurring and causing damage? And what if we determined what these higher risk issues were through the data that we collected? Suddenly our program would be addressing issues that hit home with the people in our aviation unit.

The final step is to involve the safety committee in data analysis and determination of higher risk items that should be addressed. If done right, subjectivity is quickly removed from the safety program.

4) The Safety Program Doesn't Seem to Do Anything. I am the first person to recommend getting rid of a safety procedure, tool or training if it does not work. As a current law enforcement pilot, I come to work wanting to fly as much as possible on the awesome missions we are assigned. But I want to do everything I can to make sure the people I talk to either through APSA or at my agency go home at the end of their shift. I know that I have limited time and resources to make both happen. I have no time or patience for any tactic, safety or not, that isn't working.

The problem is determining what is not working. The absence of an accident does not mean our operation is safe. We all know that. We may be spending time and money on a safety issue that seems to be preventing an accident, but in reality it may not be making a difference. However, because it is related to safety, we are reluctant to change it.

If we have begun the steps suggested, the solution to this problem is already in place. Instead of assumption, start with data. Know what risks are out there and how often they happen, and develop a strategy to address them that includes well defined goals. Aspire for something more specific than "safe operations" or "fewer accidents." When your risk assessment is done, make sure a number is associated with that risk level so you can track changes over time.

When asked if the safety program is "doing anything," we can give clear, objective answers if it is based on numbers. This performance information helps for future planning and cuts costs on wasteful training and procedures. It also helps improve the perception of the safety program.

We must also stop focusing on only accident and incident occurrences. If our agency goes a while without an accident, the impact of
safety on the absence of negative outcomes slowly becomes diminished. Federal Bureau of Investigation Safety Officer Troy Smith says
quantifying the proactive safety efforts a unit makes is a better indicator of unit safety and program performance than simply tracking
errors. The metrics are defined as "accident prevention efforts," or
APE. By tracking APE, we can evaluate the performance of the safety
program independent of the accident rate.

5) Safety Is Boring. Safety is like working out. You need to do it
often to get better. Going to the gym once a month for eight hours is
not as effective as working out 30 minutes several times a week.
There are certain kinds of workouts each person dislikes. So we have
to find something that interests us because we cannot expect to stick
with an exercise routine we hate, even if we know it is good for us.

Similarly, we cannot maintain safety vigilance if we find it painfully
boring, even if we know it is good for us. I find it much easier to put
together a class on aircrew tactics than a typical safety briefing. A
bunch of videos of bad guys hiding in the bushes or being introduced to
a K-9 is inherently fun and interesting to talk about. The connection to
our successful missions is clear and immediate.

But safety does not need to be boring. First, we must make sure we
constantly connect the safety topic we are discussing to improved operational capability. Going through the steps suggested can keep the
connection between safety and job effectiveness strong and realistic.
Use real world examples, applications and scenarios to connect the
material to each person's desired job goals.

When putting a class together, avoid slide after slide of plain text
in the exact same format. Change it up—add color and pictures. Keep
text sizes at least 20-point font or larger and do not have too much
material on each slide. Minimize safety lingo as much as possible.
There are plenty of safety related videos to accompany any topic you
may be addressing. Every eight to 10 slides, insert a short mental

break with something funny or interesting to watch. Yes, those awesome bad guy videos can work just as well in your safety presentation.

When done poorly, safety can be annoying, boring and a true waste of time. Done correctly, it can lead to more successful work, fewer injuries and less damaged equipment. The steps have been laid out before us. It is time to choose which road you want to take.

THE BEST PILOTS:
Successful Skillset Includes Learning, Listening & Lessons

What makes for the best pilot? Military trained or civilian? Sworn law enforcement or non-sworn? Large commercial operational background or stick-and-rudder general aviation experience? We can also argue about physical traits—height, vision, etc.—but I have rarely seen any pilot argue in favor of a category he or she is not in. In the end, we tend to assume pilot skill level using some combination of these characteristics and flight hours. And while they are all interesting facts about any pilot's background, none of them determine if a person will be a good public safety aviator.

The answer to what characteristics make for the best law enforcement pilots, or what criteria should be listed on job postings, is not simple or universal.

Good pilots are not born; they are made. The same holds true of tactical flight officers, mechanics, crew chiefs, rescue divers, etc. How are they made? Through training.

SAFETY LESSONS

The quality of a professional is the sum of his or her training. Training comes in many forms. Typically, we think of the formal classroom setting or the practical training we receive in our initial or commercial-level instruction. And these are important aspects of our overall education which set the foundation of our professional development. But all too often, the process stops at the foundation.

I was once asked by a fellow pilot why I was reviewing my tattered copy of a primary flight textbook. I said I liked to look over my highlighted notes from time to time as a refresher. He replied that I didn't need to "read that stuff anymore" because I already had my license. I still regret not saying anything to him—I felt it was his choice if he didn't want to study more—because two years later, he died in a loss of control accident attributed to pilot error. Would it have changed anything if I'd said something different? I'll never know. What I do know is that neither of us did everything we could to prevent the accident. We could have done more.

Motivation is critical in fighting complacency, one of the biggest concerns in aviation safety. Sometimes, motivation levels can be difficult to determine. We usually don't worry until we see errors indicating complacency is setting in. Often, these indicators become apparent because they have lead to an accident.

Voluntarily engaging in continuing education is an excellent indicator of professional motivation. Those who watch training videos online, attend seminars and conferences, read books and magazines, or participate in professional associations and meetings are not likely to be victims of complacency.

Simply performing the job is a means of training. Every time we apply our education in the real world, we understand the principles a little better than before. When we are challenged on-the-job and employ our skills, we learn. This is why experience is still an important factor in determining how "good" someone is at his or her job.

Learning everything we need to know about our profession would take a little more than a lifetime. And there are more than a few lessons we would all prefer to learn by some means other than experience—engine fires, for example. This is where additional training resources come into play. Learning from the experiences of others through their presentations, watching videos, participating in roundtable discussions and reading articles are all valuable ways to continue our education.

In 1994, I was a college student interested in law enforcement aviation. I rented a Cessna 152 and flew to Selina, KS, to attend an APSA (then ALEA) seminar. I took notes during presentations and asked questions during breaks, trying to learn as much as I could. It started a process of collecting experiences and knowledge that would keep me safe throughout my career.

By the time I had a chance to work full-time as a public safety pilot, I had the experiences of countless aviators filed away to augment my limited real-life experience. Eight years into my career, I had a partial power failure while arriving over a call location at 700 feet AGL. I was a CFI at the time and felt I knew the aircraft well. However, I had only trained for complete power failures. During the partial failure, the engine started to surge and extremely loud compressor stalls cracked continuously above our heads. The corrective action recommended in the manual did not work as advertised. I briefly sat dumbfounded. Nothing about the event fit any of the scenarios covered during my ground-based or airborne training.

Suddenly, the low rotor RPM horn sounded and drew my attention to the tachometer. The needle was plummeting down through the yellow arc. While I had never experienced anything like this before, in 2004 I had read Bill Probets' article in APSA's *Air Beat* about an engine failure he experienced. Later, I heard Probets speak about the incident. I took about 10 pages of notes during his one-hour presentation. I'd also spent five years learning to fly with Alachua County (FL) Sheriff's Office Chief Pilot Richard Bray, who had many years of experience—the "there I was" and "there someone I know was" stories he shared with me covered partial power failures and drooping rotor RPMs.

With Probets' and Bray's voices shouting in my head, I lowered the collective to recover RPMs and committed to putting the aircraft on the ground. I believe the decision prevented a rotor stall above a housing development.

Probets' article and subsequent presentation had influenced how we trained our aircrews to deal with emergency landings. The TFO was given as many tasks as possible to allow the pilot to concentrate on flying. My TFO, Ed Gazarek, had never been in a partial engine failure either. However, he did an amazing job of calling out possible landing locations and obstacles, working the radio, turning on external lights to warn traffic on the road where we were landing, etc.

Surviving the incident was all because of training that started with an 1,800-word magazine article.

The training that saved Gazarek and me that day only partially came from annual refresher training and ground school. The key training came from reading, listening to lessons learned, and having a mentor that went beyond the textbook and practical test standards.

Who is the best pilot? The best pilot is the one with the most training—training from the classroom, books, magazines, conversations, online resources and real-world experience. The best pilot has the motivation to seek out training and go beyond the minimum requirements. The best pilot is the one who doesn't think he or she is the best because there is still so much to learn. The best pilots, mechanics, TFOs and aircrew members are all of you who are reading this, because you want to get better.

LOOK UP:
You Are Contributing To An Incredible History

The most powerful perspective can be lost in an instant by the allure of an intense detail. Incredible views of the world can wash away our knowledge of the details that make them happen. This difficult balance between wide and narrow views leads to everything from spatial disorientation in the cockpit to poor policy making on the ground. It can cause our physical death or prevent us from enjoying the benefits of the life we've worked so hard to make for ourselves.

From a safety management approach, perspective can easily be lost as we focus in on individual details of an event, hazard report or procedure we are looking at. If we maintain too wide a view in risk management we may fail to understand the factors that actually contribute to failures. Statements like, "Make sure you don't make a mistake" and other similar broad statements are often an indicator of this error. On the other hand, if the focus is too narrow, a proposed risk control can be rendered ineffective because there was insufficient understanding of how it fits into the overall operation. This is when safety makes a bad name for itself as not fitting into the 'real world'.

Balance can be obtained in several ways with an effective Safety Management System (SMS). Have a safety committee composed of people representing the major job classifications of your operation. Committee members should include those involved in training, administration, maintenance, and all crew positions (TFO, crew chief, medic,

Visual Observer, etc.). The committee should set annual goals and the objectives needed to meet those goals. This list gives the safety program a perspective that includes all functions of the organization and is a tool that can be used to maintain that wholistic view throughout the year when digging into the details needed to accomplish those tasks.

Just as great paintings are made up of countless brush strokes, we will not be able to create our vision of an amazing air support unit without putting the right pieces in place. Unfortunately, proclaiming a unit will be safe and professional does not make it so. In risk management, we ensure the details are the right building blocks needed for our organization by spending some time analyzing the hazards we find. What little pieces actually contribute to the problem? Can we do better than simply blaming inevitable human error or throwing our hands up and saying it is just the cost of doing business? Usually the answer is yes, assuming we are willing to learn how to do it and take the time to do so. Simple analysis processes such as the, "5-Why's" are all we need to start painting the right brush strokes.

The world can rob our view of an incredible sunset by continually pulling our attention to the mud around our feet. Well, lately it hasn't been exactly mud, it's been worse. Please, indulge me for a bit.

When I was in my mid-20's, I was travelling to places as close to edge of the map as I could get. I had been backpacking with a fellow student for a few weeks and was starting to get impatient. Studying overseas was part of a big plan to get a career started back home and I was, in my opinion, wildly behind schedule in that endeavor. One evening we sat on a rock outcropping while I scowled at a map that gave no encouraging information on where to get the bus back towards civilization the next morning, or more immediately important, where to find something to eat. I looked at my friend and started to vocalize that we were surly going to starve to death, but stopped short when I noticed her eyes glistening with tears. I asked her what was wrong and she simply replied, "It's so beautiful." I followed her gaze to see a truly amazing sight. We were sitting on top of ancient city ruins staring at a snow-capped mountain range painted with the soft colors of sunset, laced with pure white clouds and framed below by endless miles of dark green highland plains. I was overwhelmed with shame. I'd almost missed one of the most amazing sights in my life because I was staring at the stupid map in my hand angry that the world around me wasn't what I thought it should be at that time. It was a moment of clarity that has stuck with me ever since. Sometimes when I am unhappy, or just downright angry, I hear a voice in my head that tells me to 'look up', and I'm usually made aware that I've been missing a hell of a view. It's not always the mountains in the sunset type of view, sometimes just the view of life that I've been missing while my attention was being hi-jacked by some detail.

As I write this, the world is embroiled in a series of major events that have consumed the bulk of civilization's attention. The latest is one that is extremely negative towards law enforcement. It has been weighing down on so many of us. My attention keeps being drawn to these negative...details. It may seem strange that I would call such major events details, but when I look up, I see they are small parts of something much bigger.

I have no idea what the world will look like when you get to read this. We may be back on the murder hornets for all I know. What I do know is that we are part of the amazing legacy of public safety aviation, and nothing can take that from us. Fifty years ago, this association brought us all together so we could share ideas that help us be our best and support one another through challenges and turmoil. During that time, our industry has been in a constant state of change and, because we have supported one another, we have survived massive challenges to our safety and our livelihood. And still, what we have done for the last 50 years will be legend for the rest of time. Our work chasing bad guys through the darkest nights, hoisting victims out of the clutches of death in the knick of time, finding lost children more terrified than a child should ever be, or extinguishing raging fires just as they prepare to con-sume a family's home amount to even more than the impact of each individual success. What we have done for the last 50 years has created a symbol of what people can do when they are at their best. We are still included in movies and television so often because public safety aviation is a source of awe for others. The aircraft, cameras and other gear we use are what they give to the heroes in those shows, because often they are at the leading edge of what our imagination will allow us to consider. Our industry is an inspiration for children to do something amazing with their lives. We are all of this because of the strife we have endured and conquered, not in spite of it.

What I want to say is this, "look up." For a moment at least, look away from the...mud...we have been walking through and look up to see how amazing you are and what incredible work you do. Look up at the amazing views we are gifted through the cockpit windows. Look up at the incredible technology you've created to make the world a better place. Whether you fly, fix, create gear or support this industry, look up and see that you are contributing to an incredible history. What you do is a part of the iconic image of heroic people doing heroic work that has inspired others for over 50 years. While I am unsure what the next 50 years has in store for us, I am looking forward to flying there with all of you good people.

Safety • Education & Training • Networking• Public Service
Professionalism • Ethics & Integrity

JOIN
APSA:
TO SERVE, SAVE AND
PROTECT FROM THE AIR

The Airborne Public Safety Association (APSA) is a non-profit educational, membership organization, founded in 1968. Over 3,500 members strong from the local to the international level, APSA provides networking systems, educational seminars and product expositions that members find invaluable.

APSA's mission statement is to "To support, promote and advance the safe and effective utilization of manned and unmanned aircraft by governmental agencies in support of public safety operations through training, networking, advocacy and educational programs." The safe and successful completion of each airborne public safety operation is APSA's vision statement. Would you like to join APSA?

MEMBERSHIP COSTS & GUIDELINES

An individual membership is $55 per year (North America) and $75 per year (outside of United States/Canada). Individual membership may be conferred upon any person who demonstrates an interest in public safety through advancement of the use of public aviation. *Please note that only Individuals Members who are employed or appointed by a governmental agency under the laws of any state or nation, whose duties and responsibilities include the assignment as aircrew in or supervision and management of the agency's aviation and/or alternative aircraft operations unit, section, division or department may hold the office as a director or officer of APSA.

APSA's online membership application can be found at https://publicsafetyaviation.org/membership/become-a-member/individual-membership. For questions or inquiries about APSA's individual or corporate membership, please contact APSA Headquarters at (301) 631-2406.